DREW SMITH'S
BABY
FOOD
watch

DREW SMITH'S

BABY

FOOD

watch

The surest way to feed your child healthily

HarperCollins*Publishers*

For Sue, Oliver, Grace, and George

First published in 1995
by HarperCollins*Publishers*, London

© Drew Smith 1995

The rights of Drew Smith to be identified as the Author of this
Work have been asserted by him in accordance with the
Copyright, Design and Patents Act 1988.

A CIP catalogue record for this book is available from the
British Library.

ISBN 0 00 412778 1

Printed and bound in Great Britain by HarperCollins
Manufacturing Glasgow

CONTENTS

The first sense

This is a manual on the best way to feed yourself and your new baby. By best, I mean the most nutritious, the most interesting, the most enjoyable and the best value foods in the shops.

I meant to write a book about good food; instead I have written about bad foods or foods at least that do not seem to have any meaning. Maltodextrin, for example, was only brought into use in the late '70s but is now the major ingredient in dried baby foods.

Over the last six months I have bought every baby food on the market and talked to every baby food manufacturer. I have also consulted nutritional experts, doctors, countless mums and would-be mums and read just about every publication on the subject offering what is frequently contradictory advice. Most importantly, I have also lived through the experience of bringing two children into the world.

I set out to shoot the myths from the sky surrounding baby foods, to unravel the old wives stories, work out what on earth those labels meant and come up with a reference guide to what anyone might really need to know about baby food.

Use this book and it will save you many hours of pointless shopping and a few hundred pounds in unnecessary extravagances and other rip-offs; but perhaps most importantly it will set you and your baby on the best possible nutritional path for the rest of your lives. I hope it will, indirectly, give you pleasure every time you sit down to eat.

It is important for a new baby to be introduced to as wide a range of different flavours and textures as possible. Not just because they are interesting, but because foods are part of their education in what the world they have been brought into smells and feels like. It is an introduction to what else is on this planet apart from themselves. Taste is possibly the first of all the major senses to develop.

SHOP TO DROP...

When weighed down with nappies, prams and cots and twiddly little toys in the supermarket, mothers don't really have that much time to wander around and study the difference between follow-on formula and Teatimers. The gospel of consumer choice does not really apply when you have one, or two, or even three babies in arms.

If you use this manual properly it will repay you weeks that you would otherwise have spent in car parks, pushing a trolley up supermarket aisles looking for the creche – 'what creche is that madam?' Or trying to find a loo – 'you can use the staff loo madam, but its locked and the supervisor has the key' – and a whole list of things that you really Don't Want To Be Involved With.

You might well think by the end of this book that the best buy of all is through mail order from Baby Organix and be done with the whole palava. Except, of course, that you miss out on the cut-price nappies in the supermarket.

In the beginning it was breast milk all the way, then – and some of you may find this a bit unhygenic or tricky to believe – grandma or auntie softened whatever the family was eating in her mouth before passing the morsel over to baby. Doubtless the food was a lot more interesting than semolina from a packet. The food processor may be one of the great boons to motherkind but not without some loss in terms of introducing the young taste buds to the vivid wonderful flavours that are part of this world in which we live and, also, of handing over to the baby all the antibodies and immunities that the adult's saliva contains.

THE HALF TRUTHS...

Buying baby food is not exactly easy. Manufacturers make outrageous, mindboggling claims for their products. Innocent little jars and packets declare themselves as macaroni cheese, but are nothing like any macaroni cheese that you may have encountered before. The packets and their enclosed brochures include comments such as 'avoid changing brands for no good reason'. You might be fooled into thinking that was some form of medical advice. Or there will be a bold claim that there is no sugar or no sweeteners in drinks when they are made up of glucose or sucrose which amounts to the same thing. These are not isolated examples. The practice of telling half truths is endemic. Baby food manufacturers seem to find it difficult to tell the whole truth and nothing but the truth.

A HELTER SKELTER...

To make matters still more complicated much of the food sold for babies has changed out of all recognition in the last few years. Baby foods are on a helter skelter all of their own. If you are pregnant now, then the only sure thing is that you will confront a whole new generation of baby foods to someone who had a baby even two years ago.

The old adage about asking mum has become meaningless. Your mother for certain never dealt with these new types of foods. Imagine the phone call:

– 'Mum, did you ever feed me on maltodextrin? Was it any good? No? What about whey protein? Or lecithin? Can you tell me the difference between sucrose and glucose? Does it really matter if I give the baby adult Ribena, Baby Ribena or Sugar Free Ribena?'

We are told, and I have no reason to doubt it, that these foods and drinks are safe. If you look back down the century you will find that neither the development of baby foods nor the understanding of nutrition have ever been consistently right all the time. It is hard to believe that what we are told today is set in stone either.

THE GOOD NEWS...

Many of the changes now going on are a direct response to a slack, cynical, scandalous, baby food industry being shown up for what it was. Campaigners have won important victories over hidden sugars in drinks. As I write **Farley's** has withdrawn one of its chocolate lines that was 44% sugar. The success of a small organic outfit, **Baby Organix,** has spurred the multination-

---

HOW MUCH DOES IT COST TO FEED A BABY?

Baby foods are expensive. If you were truly extravagant and bought nothing but jars of prepared meals and tetrapaks of ready made up drinks, a baby could eat its way through the best part of £1000 each year. If you don't want to breastfeed and use formual milks instead then this figure could rise to £1500. Following the advice in here will probably save you most of this cost. To put those numbers into context, **Sainsbury's** currently estimates that a family of four could eat for a year on an economical budget of about £2,500. Babies can be expensive.

Cost-wise, most outrageous of all are ready diluted drinks – usually just flavoured waters – which cost more than the equivalent of a pint of a beer or a bottle of wine.

als into producing organic ranges which, funnily enough, don't seem to need the long lists of bizarre ingredients of their main lines. Both **Safeway** and **Sainsbury** have launched own label organic lines to compete. Much of the work of the consumer campaigners on the mis-use of formula milks in the third world (and here) is filtering, albeit slowly, into legislation.

Whether in two years time it will be possible to say that the baby food industry has cleaned up its act remains an open question, even a year ago one would not have bothered to ask the question. It would have been futile.

WHAT DO BABIES REALLY WANT?

I have been surprised at how people talk about baby food. Most mothers said it was incomprehensible but necessarily bland yuk. But babies are highly sensitive to flavours and tastes. They have more tastebuds than adults – especially the ones that recognise sweet foods. Mealtimes are important pivots in their days so why not make them as interesting as possible?

The sensible advice is: when weaning, get a baby as quickly as possible from breast milk to the same food that the family eats. As far as possible these should be whole foods, freshly prepared. I would avoid all foods with colourants, flavourings, and obscure preservatives for as long as is practical. Personally, I would ban them from all baby and toddler foods.

The real advantage of nearly all the commercial foods is convenience. They do not really amount to a diet in themselves. They are for emergencies. If a child ate nothing but the packets and jars listed in this book they would be at high risk of malnutrition and certainly of losing all their teeth.

Given that warning, the dried cereals are helpful if you are on the move and in most cases are probably no worse than the breakfast cereals the rest of us eat once a day. The expensive little jars of pure fruit puree are equally handy, perhaps more so.

WHO ARE THESE PEOPLE ANYWAY?

The writing of this book has been a journey along which I have met three very different kinds of people.

The baby food manufacturers are mostly huge profit oriented multinational companies that hide behind tiers of spin doctors and glossy brochures. They claim to be experts in infant nutrition but are actually just experts in selling things.

The high priesthood of the baby food universe is a group of people who call themselves, among other things, paediatric nutritionists. They put up an invisible wall of science. It is all very well and laudable being a paediatric nutritionist in the NHS, but it is completely different working for a multi-national food company. These people tended to say things like: 'I know more than you. You would need expert advice' blah blah. None of which is much help on a Friday afternoon in Boots. Most worrying is that this group seems obsessed with justifying and sanctioning the inclusion of long lists of different foods that babies have never eaten before.

I also talked to a great many Don't Knows. Often they were people I didn't expect to be Don't Knows – doctors and nurses mainly. They said – yes, there is something here and I wish I knew. Why don't you write about it?

Do junk foods matter?

The latest research has shown that there may be a direct link between eating a highly processed diet and a mother's milk. Trans-fatty acids are usually created as a result of hydrogenation. This hardens soft fats. The government's recommendation is not to eat more than 5g a day. A convenience diet of crisps, biscuits, pies, chips, etc., represents considerably more. The concern is that such a diet dilutes a mother's milk with the result that the baby will be hungry and need supplements too early. Worse still is the theory that either through our milk or early diet we may be implanting diseases in our children that may not surface for decades.

The answer is to eat wholefoods, freshly prepared where the maximum number of original vitamins and minerals remain.

THANK YOU'S

There are also three people to whom I owe more than most for bringing this book about. My own children Oliver, who is now six, and Grace who is four, who lived through it themselves. Every time I get over zealous, they remind me that, yes, they do eat chocolate and Macdonalds and they ask awkward questions like how come daddy finished the bottle of wine last night?

And then there is George, born half way through the writing of this book, to Polly, who commissioned it, with him, I suspect in mind. I hope in some way this book helps George, and you, and your new baby to a better and more fulfilling way of life.

Everything you didn't want to
know about maltodextrin
• •

The introduction of maltodextrin in baby foods is startlingly controversial and yet has passed almost without comment. As you will see over the coming chapters, it appears with monotonous regularity as a main constituent of dried foods.

Maltodextrins are partially broken-down carbohydrates – a link, in a way, between starch and sugar. They are derived from any starch, usually from corn or potato and also, increasingly, rice. When hydrolised they turn into the gums that provide the glue on envelopes and stamps. The food business uses them partly hydrolised, mainly in sauce mixes, coffee whiteners, low fat salad dressings, sweets and frozen desserts.

The case for using maltodextrins is simple: they are a cheap, sweet bulking agent that carries other flavours well, even improving them. Maltodextrins are used in adult foods because they provide a sensual mouth feel. This is the basis for their development, in synthetic cream sweets especially and to support artificial flavours.

The case against maltodextrins is, firstly, that they are a pure additive. They contribute nothing good to the diet in themselves. Instead, they provide bulk and enhance the flavour of other ingredients – which may then be cheap, poor quality ones. And, once eaten, they are broken down to sugars.

There are two other issues of serious concern. Feeding babies on products containing maltodextrin familiarises their young taste buds with exactly the type of high additive, poor quality synthetic foods that we are all being warned against eating. Where baby food manufacturers are quick to claim their products include no additives, they often actually contain the very stuff that in later life is used to deliver those same additives.

And then, is it not amazing that, for all the controls and sensitivity over what babies should be eating, that a whole generation has now been raised on a foodstuff that no-one else in the history of the world has ever eaten? Perhaps, if it were a new, highly nutritious food, there would be a case for it. But it is not. Rather, it is probably everything that most mothers would not want their babies to eat.

A healthy
Pregnancy

In pregnancy the body starts to dictate what it needs. Beyond the usual prescription for a diet that covers the full spectrum of vitamins and minerals there are no strong guidelines at this stage as to what to eat and what not to eat.

At different times there have been fads about not eating this or that, but broadly speaking it is fitness that is important. Unless you are seriously overweight, it is probably better to eat foods that build up strength than to suddenly crash on to a low nutrition weight-loss diet. A healthy diet by definition will not let your body put on too much extra fat. Exercise is a better route to a well-tuned body, especially in the early months of pregnancy while you are still mobile, before swimming becomes the last viable option.

THE IMPORTANCE OF CALCIUM

Extra sources of calcium help build up bones. A pint of skimmed milk – you don't need the fat – a day in cereals, coffee, and sauces is a reasonable target. Other easy sources of calcium are yoghurt and hard cheeses.

GETTING INTO GOOD HABITS

Pregnancy marks the start of a period where the food you buy becomes more important. You have your own body to look after, and a new baby and probably a family too. It is a chance to get into some good habits and you may well find that your body is already starting to let you know the kind of foods it wants. There are no quick fixes but, equally, there are no cardinal sins. We are plotting a strategy here.

The case for
healthy eating

Good food is simply food that is good for us. Usually that means that the foods will be as close to their original form as possible – a whole orange, for example, is better nutritionally than orange juice.

The famous cravings for the more bizarre foods like chocolate or even coal are the body asking for more of one mineral or vitamin than another. A varied diet should give your body all the nourishment it needs. The new baby may well be hungry for vitamins of its own and this may account for your changing tastes through pregnancy. Most of the nutrition you and your baby need, even the notorius *cause celebre* iron, can be found in everyday foods without reverting to supplements.

Men may be able to walk on the moon but for the most part they have not succeeded in improving the nutritional values of most foods by mucking around with them. They might have made them more fun, and more expensive, but prawn cocktail crisps and the Marmite-flavoured cheddar have yet to match the nutritional quality of whole wheatgerm or a peach. And for all the billions of pounds spent on research and marketing across the globe to find a substitute, no company has as yet produced a milk that is as good for a baby as breast milk.

Our bodies are often a good guide in themselves, if we listen to them. Before I started this book I spent a whole week in which I ate nothing and drank only water and lemon barley. Towards the end, it was not the cream cakes or fillet steaks that I craved, just a simple wholemeal roll. I can still taste it now. It was among the most wonderful things I have ever eaten. I was hungry for the nutrition in it. Advertising sells foods on the presumption that we all crave certain things – like cream; or that we should somehow aspire to spread I Can't Believe It's Not Butter on our toast. We have become accustomed to toxins in our diet from drinks like coffee.

It is often too easy to overlook that in a well-tuned diet, it is the staples – bread, potatoes, rice and pasta – that are important. The ratio of rice to meat in eastern diets is arguably much more satisfying and beneficial than the western indulgence of hunks of steak with a pile of chips. The body seems to want to form habits – like craving sugar, or even just wants the bulk volume in some foods. But these are very short-lived cravings, and are even shorter-lived if instead you eat foods that compete not only nutritionally but also in flavour and interest. That is what good cooking is all about. If you de-tox your body for a couple of days – say just eat fruit and drink water – it is surprising how swiftly the responses change and how apparent it becomes that a great many of the things we have all become accustomed to are mildly addictive. I am steering a path well away from slimming foods because most of them are also addictive. Slimming and good diet are different disciplines.

What is a *balanced diet?*

A balanced diet is a cliché. In fact, it is the cliché that allows just about any company to say just about anything it likes about its product. The idea of balance is imbalanced.

Even a company like **Sainsbury**'s, where you might expect ideas on modern nutrition to be advanced, can proclaim that it sells 'a healthy shopping basket for a family of four for £46 a week that conforms to the government's Health of the Nation guidelines'. And yet this same shopping basket is loaded up with jam rolls, a carton of cream, chocolate biscuits, tarts, crisps, choc-ices and chocolate. Although this basket may or may not conform to the guidelines, if this government, or Sainsbury's, really believe such things are healthy then heaven help us. If you were a nutritional nun and had eaten nothing but whale liver, live yoghurt, soya bean salads and pineapples for most of your life, then perhaps a few days mainlining on Bounty Bars, crunching on meringues and washing the frying pan out with double cream wouldn't do

---

BEST BUYS

There is only one food on the market specifically designed for mothers-to-be. **Boots** produce 250g cartons of fortified milk drink reinforced with folic acid. The drink also contains calcium, thiamin, riboflavin, and B12. There is strawberry or banana flavour and it is recommended that it be served chilled, which usually means the drink doesn't taste that great at room temperature. Like many Boots foods, they are almost medicines.

---

you much harm, apart from perhaps making you sick. That's the compromise.

Of course, it is a balanced diet in the sense that it has got enough essential vitamins and minerals, but it is low rent nutrition – bottom of the class stuff. It is not even particularly cheap. Ready-made cottage pies are hugely expensive compared to buying the ingredients and cooking at home.

It illustrates well how the whole healthy eating message has been turned into a meaningless pantomime. There is the old-fashioned paternalistic attitude that if you are going to buy one healthy thing, say rice, then it will have to be offset with something 'naughty', or 'wicked' or 'nice' to compensate. The classic guilt trip.

Shopping For Good Foods

Nearly eighty per cent of the foods necessary for a healthy diet can be found in the first aisle of the bigger supermarkets – fresh fruit, fresh vegetables, rice, pasta and often fresh fish. If it wasn't for the loo rolls and the bottle of wine, you might almost stop there. Whether this is psychological positioning by the supermarkets or good commerce is not clear.

The best foods are without doubt whole foods – still in their natural, even raw state. In nearly every case any amount of refining or even cooking starts to detract from the nutritional value.

A history of *British diet*

The British diet was never thought out. There probably never was a time when it was balanced. This is a northerly country where the climate has never been helpful in growing crops and raising livestock. When the Romans first came here they brought with them many of their own foods and the last two millenia have seen the traffic in cereals, vegetables and fruit coming north from Europe, rather than the other way round. Meat is the one exception to that rule.

What we call British food was a panic reaction to how to feed the hundreds of thousands who moved from the country to the cities in the industrial revolution. Its first contribution to nutrition was the gin palace and it might not be over cynical to suggest that it has largely carried on in the same vein for 200 years. Politicians and industry colluded because they had to. In a democracy the only person who fears empty shelves in the shops more than the grocer is a politician.

Food became an instrument of colonial foreign policy.

It has only been the rise of the modern-day supermarket since the '80s – Sainsbury, Tesco, Waitrose, Marks and Spencer and Safeway – that has given consumers real choice in what they eat. Before then, most people's diets were restricted to what their local corner shop stocked which, in comparison, was not very much. For the first time in the '80s, people started to go to shops with 15,000 foods or more in one place. They could make an intelligent choice for themselves, which is really what this book is about.

Mum *wasn't right after all*

What is interesting is that, when people actually had the choice, they started to buy more fresh fruit and vegetables. Staples like pasta and rice featured more prominently. In addition, Indian food – with its emphasis on rice and vegetables – for eating at home is the fastest single growth area of any food in the last year.

People did not stock up on cakes and biscuits. It is tempting to argue that the great biscuit and jam diet earlier this century was comfort eating in the face of austerity. When people got the chance to buy wholesome foods, they did so instinctively.

I am dwelling on this history only to stress the point that we are probably the first generation ever to have this freedom. There is no need to feel guilty about dumping most of the pre-1980 advice on what to feed yourself or your baby in

---

WHAT TO AVOID WHEN YOU ARE PREGNANT

In the early stages of pregnancy it is quite common to experience a burning in the stomach, which is the acid rising up. In later pregnancy, it can actually be the womb pressing on the stomach and pushing the acid up. Spicy, fatty and highly seasoned foods are said to aggravate this. Eating a little and often through the day can help ease the sensation.

Alcohol is a well-known aggravant too, passing through the bloodstream to the foetus which finds itself swilling around in white wine. Not for nothing was gin called mother's ruin. Coffee and tea are often discouraged because of the caffeine but as the often quoted limit is not more than seven cups a day this hardly represents severe deprivation.

the dustbin. Mum is not necessarily right. She was right for her time. The world is a better place and your baby is going to get a better chance than you did.

So what is a *healthy diet?*

Some foods we know are good for us. Everything else is not exactly bad for us, but it is just simply unimportant. The problem with the classic British diet is the problem with the UK food industry: most of the foods produced fall into the second category, while the sources of many of the foods in the first category – orchards, rivers, inshore fishing, oat fields, etc. – have been or are being abandoned.

Cooking often detracts from the nutritional value of many foods. Some of the most persuasive diets concentrate on raw foods for that reason. The inspired Leslie Kenton even goes as far as recommending a diet of 75% raw foods, which is great in a hot summer but somewhat less practical in a snowy, wet February. Steaming and microwaving are the healthiest ways of cooking vegetables. Cook them in a minimum amount of water with the lid on the pan. Non-stick pans offer the chance to cook without any fat at all.

If you are not going to fall back on vegetable oil or butter, then you will have to compensate with other seasonings like herbs and spices to lend their flavours. If there is one big difference in the style of cooking now, it is that the seasonings tend to go on a dish at the end – a scattering of parsley over steamed cour-

---

THE CASE AGAINST SLIMMING

Slimming diets presume that you are healthy to start with and would be a lot healthier if you were a few pounds lighter, that a few days of austerity won't do you any harm and any means will do. Suddenly the idea of a completely useless biscuit or drink becomes a virtue rather than a nonsense. In a sensible healthy diet there is not much point messing about with non-foods or foods that are not positively good for us. Most people are overweight because they eat too much. There is a simple answer to that. Reducing the calories without reducing the volume is missing the point. What we want are foods that taste good, are interesting to eat, a pleasure to handle and also nutritionally worthwhile.

gettes, a vinaigrette and chives over new potatoes – whereas traditionally the bouquet garni was dropped in at the start.

There are two ways of looking at food. They are both right in their own ways. One says we have never had it so good. The shops have never been so well supplied with so many different, affordable, interesting brands. There has never been so much whole food available.

The other says, yes OK, but what a pity that 90% of it is rubbish. And have you seen the research figures from Hackney that show that a quarter of all teenage girls have a diet so deficient nutritionally that they would damage their baby's health if they got pregnant? And what about the links of diet to cancer, heart disease and other obesity-related illnesses? And why has the Department of Health given £50,000 to an action group against sugar in baby drinks?

The values *we pass on*

The health arguments about diet are only partially convincing in themselves. In life, there is usually time enough to balance what we eat as we go. Diet will affect how our bodies perform. Within broad tramlines – say using olive oil instead of lard to cook with – there is agreement on what is good food.

What is more worrying is that trading down from high quality, traditional food businesses we know to have a long term value, to factories where work is often uncreative and poorly paid, produces foods of marginal nutritional value. Food is an important bonding, both socially and economically. No society can afford to lose sight of this. If you think I am overstating the case, then look what has happened to the Soviet Union or parts of Africa.

These considerations are important when we are talking about a new life and how we are going to introduce a baby to this slapdash old planet of ours. They are important because they are about the kind of values we are going to pass on, and food is one way to do this. Organic food is an apt example. It is not the taste that matters necessarily but the philosophy behind it. Organic food has successfully energised the commercial baby food market and made many big companies clean up their acts.

7 key
foods

1 **FRUIT** is probably the most enjoyable and healthy food, and one area where there is every reason to be extravagant. The big supermarkets have invested heavily in this area and have consciously and laudably stuck with buying class one fruit. On a wider scale, the fact that peaches are now freely available through the summer or that citrus fruit can be bought through the winter contributes to a healthy diet. The best quality fruit tends to come from France, although often at a premium price. American fruit tends to look better than it tastes. Huge quantities of fruit, of varying quality, come from Spain and Italy.

Bananas, apples and pears are classic weaning foods – although it is best not to feed babies too much high-acidity fruit. Fresh fruit is a better buy than juices, and frozen or tinned fruit. Not only is it rich in vitamins and minerals but it is increasingly being seen as an important facilitator of anti-oxidants. Exotic fruit like mangoes can be expensive but are not marked up in price in the same way as processed foods.

2 **VEGETABLES**, like fruit, provide a natural source of vitamins and minerals. Cooking tends to leach some of these. The big vitamin givers, like carrots and celery, are excellent as raw juices if you are prepared to invest in a juicing machine. Avocados are one of the most popular baby foods, used particularly for weaning babies in producing countries. You don't even need a blender for them, although they discolour if exposed to the light for any length of time. Most avocados are sold unripe and have to be ripened off on a windowsill or by putting them next to ripe fruit. Other, often overlooked, vegetables that are excellent baby foods are sweet potatoes, pumpkins, kohlrabi and squashes. These are cheap, nutritious, need only simple steaming and bring variety to meals.

3 **HERBS** and seasonings seem expensive. They interact so well with plainer foods like pulses, they should earn their place on even the strictest budget. Fresh herbs are expensive but still a better buy than dried for a one-off treat. English cookery books are always mean with the amount of herbs. A few little flecks of green as garnish is not going to do very much for anyone. If you are going to invest in fresh herbs, use them and be done with it – a whole plant at a time, or at least a good handful. If they make a dish of pulses taste wonderful then you will save the money on the pulses.

Other seasonings are worth investing in because they repay themselves many times over. Cooking salt is just as good as table salt but quite a few pence cheaper. The finest sea salt costs ten times as much, but even then it will be used for perhaps three months. Find the best kinds of mustards, soy sauce, capers that will give your cooking an edge and individuality. They repay the investment.

The larder is no place to economise. A rhizome of ginger or a bunch of fresh garlic will enliven your cooking many times over. A good larder can make salads come alive. Cheap vinegar is another useless saving. Sherry vinegars, even the rather weak balsamics now found in supermarkets, or named wine vinegars not only transform salads but can make sauces in their own right.

4 **STAPLES** like bread, potatoes, rice and pasta are the kind of foods that will respond to the herbs and seasonings and repay the investment. Invariably they are cheaper in bulk. Rice and pasta are economical because they can also be used effectively with smaller amounts of more expensive items like meat. This makes sense both nutritionally and financially. Bread is often overlooked these days as a cooking ingredient but can go for stuffing a roast; be used in gratins; and bulk out stews. The better the quality of the bread, the less likely it is you will have to smear it with butter and jam to make it palatable. That is especially true of the genuine (English bakers tend to call any long thin loaf French) French loaves – the French rarely put butter on the table at all; and also Italian breads like ciabbatta and foccaccia.

Brown bread has come to be a catch-all word for any bread that isn't white or wholemeal and can vary substantially in the amount of wheatgerm left in. Wholemeal bread is the best and, unlike the equivalent brown rice and wholemeal pasta, usually tastes better than the ordinary versions.

5 FISH should be eaten three times a week. The best from a nutritional point of view, and often inexpensive, are the oily fish like mackerel, herring and kippers (much better on the bone\than as fillets, though more expensive). Pilchards in tins are the cheapest of all and, like sardines, maintain much of their nutrients despite the canning. Tuna is the one fish that suffers in processing and is a shadow of its former self in a tin.

The easiest way to cook fish is wrapped in cling film (to retain its juices) in the microwave.

6 MEAT is a prime source of nutrients but it is expensive and imbalances the diet – nutritionally and financially – if it is eaten every day in any quantity. The old adage about meat and two veg is better turned around as two vegetables with some meat. Like fish, it is probably best eaten just three times a week and, even then, not always as big slabs. Try little shards and cubes of bacon used in, say, rice or a salad, or slices of pork or beef in a stir-fry with vegetables, or bolognese with pasta.

7 OILS AND FATS are the most contentious area. Much of the discussion is dominated by the slimming industry so that low-fat spreads are sold as if they are good nutritionally when, in fact, the fats are hydrogenated (hardened), which turns them from unsaturated (good for you) to saturated (bad for you).

❖ **Margarine** sells itself by claiming added vitamin A. One carrot contains almost the same amount of vitamin A as a whole pack of margarine.

❖ **Oil** The best oil is virgin olive oil (olive oil is a refined blend with only a limited and unspecified amount of virgin olive oil in it), which has been shown to be used in areas where the instances of western diet-related heart diseases have remained low for decades. Its disadvantage is that it is fattening. It also seems expensive but, as it can be used over many weeks, the outlay is relative. Single estate virgin olive oil from Tuscany is the best quality (different estates and regions make markedly different oils), while the best value oils are currently from Greece, especially those sold in Greek delicatessens who often undercut supermarkets by three and four times. Good olive oil is a sauce in itself. A good oil – especially a Ligurian oil – poured over grilled fish is all that is needed.

❖ **Butter** still seems to be the original article and all the arguments for other kinds of spread are usually based on price. Most spreads have just been blended with water so that, in practice, the saving is an illusion – you are paying less for less. The saving is better directed to seeking out more interesting bread.

BEATING CONSTIPATION

The hormonal changes in pregnancy can themselves lead to constipation. This can be countered with fibrous foods – wholemeal bread, pulses, even more fruit (in desperation there is always stewed prunes) and at least two pints of liquid a day. Stewed fruits can be made more interesting by using light infusions of tea rather than water. Colourful fruits like pomegranates lend character to the more industrious merits of figs and apricots.

Pulses are cheaper bought dried than in tins – lentils are the cheapest and most practical. The best lentils are the slate grey from Puy. They do not need soaking and will cook in 20 minutes (add chopped onion). If they are too bland, add a dash of soy, tomato paste, or Lea and Perrins to the water. Better still, add some stock or bones.

Cannellini are probably the finest pulse. They need soaking overnight and simmering for as long as an hour and half. The cooking water makes a good vegetarian stock. They have an uncanny affinity to good virgin olive oil and a handful of the chopped leafy green herbs such as coriander, parsley or basil.

The food
pharmacy...

We live in a drug culture. We arrest or accelerate fertility, take pills for headaches, for stomach aches or because we can't sleep. We have social drugs like alcohol and nicotine, and unsocial drugs like heroin. A great many of these drugs are just more intense versions of what is found in nature.

Nearly all the vitamins, minerals and other elements that our bodies need are found scattered across the aisles of the supermarket. They do not have to come in neat little packages marked, say, vitamin C – an orange does fine. A balanced diet picks up all the vital nutrients from a whole spectrum of foods, each of which contributes different elements, in varying degrees. Often each food contributes only very small quantities of a particular element but they all build up during the day, and through the week, to form the vital building blocks of life. This variety is immensely important in itself. It makes what we eat more entertaining and ensures our bodies get all the nutrients they need.

NUTRITIONAL LOOPHOLES

Nutritional labelling usually refers not just to uncooked foods but foods in good condition. Nutrients are lost in storage. A potato straight out of the ground is likely to have a higher density of nutrients than one that has been stored through the winter. Buy seasonal produce because it is nutritionally sound, invariably cheaper and also has more flavour.

The great achievement of the supermarket culture has been to make a healthy diet available to nearly everyone. There is less need for vitamin and mineral supplements when these same nutrients are widely available as part of our diet. There is also less need to buy foods with vitamins added, when those foods which contain vitamins naturally are sitting on the next shelf.

Old-fashioned *causes*

The great nutritional causes of this century – like making sure that everyone drinks milk, so that we get enough calcium and don't suffer from rickets – are still valid but not necessarily as valid as when they were dreamed up. There are often better sources of nutrients now.

When my daughter, Grace, was born four years ago, there were no organic baby foods on the market and no own-labels. Now three supermarkets do own-label baby foods and nearly every major brand has an organic range.

In a normal diet today, with cheese and coffee, we would expect to obtain sufficient calcium. Vitamin D supplements belong to an era of families growing up in northern winters who spent most of their time indoors and rarely saw the sunlight or had access to fresh vegetables. Today most families go out into the sun and can buy fresh vegetables. It cannot be very long before we can actually buy cod liver itself, rather than the oil. Iodine used to be added to salt to protect against goitre – in fact, it is still added to some brands – although most of us are protected through our milk intake or, in the

---

SUPERMARKETS: THE GOOD AND THE BAD

The supermarkets split into two groups: the big five, to which I might add newer branches of Somerfield and larger branches of the Co-op, and the others, who lag behind. The difference is simply in how much fresh food they sell and how many foods they sell that help you to cook – for example, olive oil, vinegar and different kinds of butter. A bad supermarket is one that is stacked high with tins and packets and where most of the foods are what the trade calls 'high value added' – i.e. cheap ingredients, fancy packaging, low nutrition and big mark-up. These are supposedly cheap but, in reality, are poor value.

case of vegans, through seaweed. We have moved out of the Victorian era of packing up singular commodities, into an era of a global fresh food economy.

Are you getting *enough vitamins?*

Nearly all the vitamins and minerals we need can now come from what we eat. Foods are at their richest nutritionally when they are raw and lose some of their value in cooking. Highly processed foods like breakfast cereals will often have extra vitamins added to justify their place at the breakfast table as 'part of a nutritionally balanced diet', but these claims are increasingly spurious. Think of your diet as a means in itself of maintaining your body at peak condition. There is no reason to spend money on low-value foods simply enriched with one or two supposedly important vitamins.

When you are *pregnant*

There is a temptation when you are pregnant and about to pass through the hands of the Great Medical Profession, and quite likely to be helped by the Wonder Drugs of Science, to believe that this will be the way of all things in the future. You also want your new baby to start out with the best, purest forms of nutrition. This is quite right but, better than pills, prescriptions and packets, are simple fresh foods.

The modern danger is that we eat a diet that is seemingly full of everything but is actually poor in essential nutrients and overloaded with inessential nutrients, leading to obesity or a recurrence of old-fashioned diseases.

WHY YOU NEED FOLIC ACID

Folic acid plays an important part in the development of the baby's brain, especially in the last three months of pregnancy and the early months of breastfeeding. Natural sources of folic acid include brown bread, green vegetables, especially spinach and cabbage, breakfast cereals, particularly wheat-germ, eggs, oily fish, cod liver oil, borage seed oil and starflower oil.

The link between
flavour and nutrition

There must be a link between flavour and nutrition, or perhaps flavour is our bodies' natural response to one food against another.

Understanding our ability to taste may have much to do with interpreting what our bodies are saying to us. We confuse messages to our bodies in the following ways:

❖ eating foods that have no nutritional value
❖ allowing ourselves foods and drinks that tend to be addictive
❖ obliterating our sense of taste by eating foods that have 100 times more intense, but artificial, flavours than are found in natural foods

All these tendencies destablilise our bodies so that we lose one of our prime radars to discern good, nutritional food.

With babies this becomes a major issue. If they do not learn how to interpret what they eat – for example, because we give them over-sugared drinks or sweets before they have a chance to taste the more subtle flavour of the original food – then they may be irreparably damaged in their relationship with food, and this will have an impact on their bodies in later life.

The studies on obesity in America, the statistics of poorly nourished teenagers here and the impact on health care point to the dangers of highly processed foods consumed in large quantities. Natural, whole and raw foods are better, not out of some romantic notion about the good old days, but because whole foods have survived the litmus test of generations.

Many of the baby food products listed in this book use substances that may make you wonder whether they are at all appropriate for babies. Doubtless they are safe and, in the main, not actually bad for your baby, but they do not have the strength of history on their side. In order to take an extra dose of vitamin C, is it right that a baby should have to swallow maltodextrin? How many people would know what maltodextrin is?

It is not progress to pump third-rate ingredients full of vitamins into foods and suggest that, therefore, these foods are worthwhile nutritionally. They are not. To aim such messages at babies and young children is manipulative and exploitative.

The
superfoods
. . . .

If your weekly shopping trolley contains half of the foods listed here, then the chances are that you do not need any foods with advertised supplements.

These lists are meant to be used as broad brushstrokes. They can guide your cooking along the right lines. Two foods which are excellent sources of different vitamins and minerals for babies, but are rarely quoted because they have only recently become part of our diet, are avocado and sweet potato.

VITAMIN A looks after the skin and eyesight. It is found in:

❖ Citrus fruits such as oranges and lemons
❖ Tomatoes
❖ Dark green, leafy vegetables like cabbage, broccoli and beans
❖ Colourful vegetables like cauliflower, sweetcorn and, of course, particularly strongly in carrots
❖ Sweet potatoes

A child under one year will need about half the amount of vitamins to the mother. He might eat half a canteloupe melon, two tablespoons of red pepper and one cup of spinach or kale to obtain the right level of vitamin A.

Margarine – a source of Vitamin A?

Many claims are made for margarine where vitamin A is added. However, you would have to eat one third of a packet (urgh) a day to keep up an adult's recommended daily intake of vitamin A. A single carrot contains as much vitamin A as a whole packet of margarine. Other preferable sources are sweet potatoes and pumpkins; even cooked, one of these has eight times the recommended daily vitamin A intake.

VITAMIN B covers a range of different vitamins, all of which are important for the nervous system. It is found in:

❖ Milk
❖ Yeast extracts
❖ Eggs
❖ Seeds
❖ Leafy green vegetables
❖ Nuts
❖ Grains
❖ Vegetables
❖ Wheatgerm

VITAMIN B12 FOR VEGETARIANS

It is important for vegetarians to keep up their intake of B12, which is often added to vegetarian foods. That said, the body stores B12 so it is not an everyday concern. Specifically, good sources of this form of vitamin B are:

❖ Cheese
❖ Eggs

❖ Some breakfast cereals
❖ Yeast extracts

And for the vegetarian baby...

Milk contains B12, although boiling will destroy it. If you are adamant about bringing up your baby as a vegan then supplements of B12 are usually recommended by doctors as a precaution against deficency.

THE OTHER B VITAMINS are often quoted by their names rather than their numbers:

Thiamin is B1 and is badly affected by cooking, as well as by drinks and foods such as tea, alcohol and raw fish. However, the following contain significant amounts of thiamin:

❖ Grains and flours
❖ Pulses

❖ Nuts

Riboflavin is B2 and survives cooking. The body does not make riboflavin, it needs to be replenished in the diet through:

❖ Cheese
❖ Milk
❖ Sweet potatoes
❖ Spinach

❖ Breakfast cereals often have added B2
❖ Nuts (almonds have especially high levels of thiamin)

Niacin is B3 and is widely found in staples such as:

❖ Pasta
❖ Potatoes
❖ Rice

❖ Peanuts are also an optimum source

Vitamin B6 is destroyed in the light. Good sources are:

❖ Avocados
❖ Sweet potatoes
❖ Seeds
❖ Nuts

❖ Vegetables (although it is argued that the sources in cereals and in yeast products are more easily assimilated by the body)

Folate is B9 and from the Latin for leaf. Raw sources contain the best levels of folate, which is found in:

❖ Spinach   ❖ Seeds
❖ Cabbage   ❖ Beans

VITAMIN C looks after the skin and gums, and also helps the body to absorb iron from other foods. It has been aggrandised to one of the key vitamins we need. Our bodies do not synthesize vitamin C, so we need to ensure a regular intake. It is a fragile vitamin, wilting in the light and in heat. Meat and dairy products have little vitamin C and neither do processed foods. It is often found in the same foods as vitamin A:

❖ Leafy green vegetables   ❖ Potatoes
❖ Citrus fruits

DURING PREGNANCY AND BREASTFEEDING

Vitamin C is especially important in pregnancy. The body's intake should go up to around 90mg a day, compared to 60mg a day for most adult women and 30mg a day for babies under a year.

Many new generation imports are also high in vitamin C:

❖ Peppers   ❖ Guava
❖ Kiwi   ❖ Chicory
❖ Kohlrabi (even   ❖ Broccoli
   cooked)   ❖ Kale (retains its
❖ Breadfruit   vitamin C if
❖ Mangoes   cooked only
❖ Papaya   lightly)

Although we have come to think of it as normal, the wealth of citrus fruits through the winter was an important dietary innovation. For babies born in winter, the worst months were always the end of February and March, when there is so little growing. In rural communities nettles – the first growth of the year – were turned into a soup as a first source of vitamin C. Even now, many of the fruits and vegetables available have been stored and will be considerably less beneficial than when they are in season. To compensate, drink juices which may have lost some, but not all, such as:

❖ Grapefruit   ❖ Passionfruit
❖ Cranberry   ❖ V8
❖ Tomato

Calcium and Phosphorus are the main building elements of bones. Most foods contain phosphorus. Calcium sources are:

❖ Milk

❖ Milk products like cheese

Modern thinking has it that absorbing calcium from a range of different foods may be important to ensure the body picks up the full range of nutrients. Other sources of calcium include:

❖ Molasses (a particularly rich source of calcium)
❖ Kale (as above)   ❖ Potatoes   ❖ Cornbreads
❖ Leafy dark green vegetables

Alternative vegan sources of calcium include:

❖ Tahini

❖ Nut milks

VITAMIN D allows the body to absorb calcium, which helps the growth of bones and teeth. Our bodies actually make vitamin D from the sunlight on our skin. One of the arguments used against breastfeeding in northern countries was that breast milk might be deficient in vitamin D if the mother was deficient, as it would be if she always wore dark clothes and stayed indoors. Current thinking says that, even at UK levels of sunlight, exposing the face and hands to the sun for 10-15 minutes every day through the summer will be enough to store up a bank of vitamin D to see you through the winter. Prime sources of vitamin D are:

> ### CALCIUM LOSS
>
> Limiting the loss of calcium from the body, rather than overloading it with new supplies which are often high in fat anyway, is important. Calcium loss in the body may well be associated with high intakes of caffeine and alcohol, as well as with lack of sunlight, lack of vegetables in the diet and lack of exercise. Meat is no longer considered an optimum source of calcium in itself.

❖ Oily fish like herring and mackerel
❖ Eggs   ❖ Milk

It is also found in butter and added to margarine and many breakfast cereals. Multi-vitamin mixes usually contain vitamin D too. Vitamin D is one of the more toxic vitamins, so too much can be damaging. There is a move to define it by its other name, Calciferol, to avoid confusion. Essentially, if there is a risk of deficiency, supplements are important. But, without special circumstances, the diet should supply the necessary quantity. You only need to increase your intake of Vitamin D:

❖ If you are breastfeeding
❖ If you live in the north
❖ If you get little sunlight
❖ If you have dark skin pigmentation

VITAMIN E is the now famous vitamin associated with anti-oxidants and the Mediterranean diet. It seems to be the most important vitamin for allowing other vitamins – particularly vitamin A – to do their work. It prevents blood clotting and, in helping the circulation of the blood, defends against the hardening of arteries. It is found in:

❖ Cereal seed oils, notably extra virgin olive oil; also corn and soya oils
❖ Vegetables

IRON is used by the body to make red blood cells which carry oxygen. It is one of the key vitamins you need in pregnancy to avoid anaemia. The ability to absorb iron increases in pregnant women so that you don't need supplements through pregnancy. The recommended daily iron intake for women is much higher than for men, because of the loss of blood in menstruation. You and your baby can acquire iron naturally from:

❖ Dried fruits (soak for a baby)
❖ Pulses
❖ Green vegetables
❖ Avocado
❖ Tomato Purée
❖ Parsley
❖ Meat, especially liver
❖ Molasses
❖ Seeds
❖ Tofu
❖ Pizza
❖ Soya flour
❖ Baby cereals are often fortified with iron

In small quantities, iron is present in foods as various as:

❖ Peanut butter
❖ Baked beans
❖ Cabbage

It is also present in high levels in foods that we only use small amounts of:

❖ Thyme
❖ Ginger
❖ Tomato paste
❖ Cocoa
❖ Sesame seeds
❖ Shellfish

HOW MUCH IRON DOES YOUR BABY NEED?

Babies are born with their own store of iron, although they tend to use it up by about four to six months. They need to get it from their diet, which is one reason that cow's milk is not usually recommended for babies. It is hard to recognise if your baby is short of iron, although lack of iron in the diet will affect development. It is not just the quantity of iron that is important, but also the baby's ability to absorb it. Vitamin C helps the body absorb the iron.

The American company, SMA, exploits this potential danger to sell its products, pointing out that in some UK groups of children between six months and five years old nearly half may be deficent in iron. This statistic is based on 1986 research, which reminds doctors and health workers in alarmist terms that deficiency may lead to a whole basketful of implied dangers: from impaired behavioural and mental development to poor weight gain and anaemia.

VITAMIN K looks after the normal clotting of the blood. Babies are not born with vitamin K but have to generate it for themselves. Historically this ability probably came from either a small amount of the mother's faeces touched in the birth or from the breast milk. The sanitisation of giving birth in hospitals, with the fad for giving enemas, has meant that sometimes the birth is just too clean for the new baby's stomach to create these natural colonies. Hospitals have had to revert to giving injections of vitamin K instead. Vitamin K is present in:

❖ Spinach (particularly high levels)
❖ Cabbage
❖ Soya beans
❖ Soya-based products like milk and yoghurt

SODIUM AND POTASIUM balance the body's fluids. Potassium is found in most foods. Sodium is found in:

❖ Bread
❖ Cereals
❖ Milk

To breastfeed
or not?

• •

For a community it must be a better goal for most women to breastfeed as a matter of normal practice than not. There is a huge social gulf in terms of overcoming ignorance – women's as well as men's.

After sitting on the jury, as it were, hearing the arguments for and against breastfeeding, I am pretty much convinced that the case for breastfeeding is proved. You might think that is a bit easy or a bit cheeky coming from a man. What right have I got, after all, to sentence the sisterhood to a term of demand feeding? The issues have not been properly presented. They certainly never were to me when our children were born. And breastfeeding has fallen out of fashion, mostly for the wrong reasons.

That does not solve the great dilemma of The Job versus The Pump versus The Baby. The answer is probably that attitudes need to change in the Work Place. And they are not going to change until everyone stops being so feckless and fey about breastfeeding.

The individual problems – which I would not want to belittle – are almost certainly overwhelmed by the greater good of living in a society where breastfeeding is accepted as a normal part of life, rather than the other way around.

Interestingly, many mothers I spoke to said the pressure not to breastfeed was often stronger from women than men. Attitudes need to change in public places to allow women to breastfeed more freely and comfortably. Creches in supermarkets, offices and factories are one answer. A more serious and understanding attitude to the whole idea of maternity and paternity leave would be another significant step forward.

About
breast milk
• •

The breasts are normally inhibited from giving milk by the action of certain hormones. These are lost in the afterbirth. So a mother is starting to make milk from the moment of delivery.

The first milk is a clear yellowish liquid called colostrum, which is rich in protein, vitamins and minerals, like zinc, low in fat and easily digested. From about the third day after delivery, the milk gets thinner as its composition changes and does not become mature breast milk until around the tenth day. By then, the colour will have changed to white.

At the start of a feed is the foremilk, which allows a baby to quench his thirst. It is followed by the hind milk, which has more energy than the foremilk. Midwives advise letting a baby finish one breast before starting on the other.

Human milk is very close to cow's milk, with a fat level of around 3.7%. The disadvantage of cow's milk for babies is that it tends to have too much protein and sodium, and too little iron or vitamins A, C or D. Often not recommended until a baby is a year old, it can happily be used in cooking instead of water.

DOES BREASTFEEDING WORK AS A CONTRACEPTIVE?

Doctors have played a part in suggesting that breastfeeding does not work as a contraceptive – or at least is not infallible. However, the studies may be flawed in a number of ways – for example, if the breastfeeding cycle is interrupted to allow drinks of water and liquid foods, the contraceptive cycle is broken.

Today's evidence suggests that provided the baby suckles for more than 65 minutes every 24 hours it is unlikely that a woman will ovulate. This appears to hold good for at least six months. Statistically only one in ten women will ovulate before her next period, and these are mainly women who have gone on breastfeeding for more than six months. The cycle breaks down the moment other foods and drinks are introduced.

---

7 Reasons why Breastfeeding
fell out of fashion

The decline in breastfeeding is linked statistically to the rise in childbirth in hospitals. Like most statistics, this suggests only one part of the story. There are many reasons why confidence in breastfeeding has been undermined.

1 **In the '50s and '60s many of the benefits of breastfeeding were poo-pooed,** not necessarily by doctors but by other health workers. Many new mothers got their first advice on how to feed a baby from a midwife or health visitor, or from their own mother or sister who may have had similar advice. This began a trend which is only recently changing, although it persists worldwide.

2 **There were social reasons.** As families got smaller and more distant, women rarely saw other women breastfeeding. They did not know how to breastfeed properly because they had no role models. Suddenly, amid everything else, they were expected to learn a whole new experience with a precious new person, and to do it wonderfully right from the start. It is hardly surprising if few of them got an alpha double plus on the first day and then felt guilty.

3 **There was no family wisdom to offset the great myths of Overfeeding or Underfeeding.** The commonest excuse women gave for abandoning breastfeeding was that the baby was not getting enough milk. With hindsight we now know that many women gave up breastfeeding because they were not doing it right – not holding the baby properly so that it could feed comfortably. Modern research also suggests that a lot of babies were probably doing fine following their own natural rythmn and that, had the mothers persevered, there would have been no harm and, quite likely, a more beneficial experience for both.

4 **Topping up babies' diets with drinks and formulas made the situation worse.** The extra food satiated the baby's hunger and set mother and baby on an irreversible path towards separation.

5 **Stress is another factor and often the main cause of milk drying up.** The more anxious a mother might be about breastfeeding, or of where she is breastfeeding, the more likely that it will interfere with the flow of milk.

6 **Sex is another issue.** Men might feel jealous of all the attention now being focused on the baby. Or the increasing sexual focus on breasts can create a rather bizarre dilemma between child and lover.

7 **Some myths were patently invented by companies seeking to persuade mothers to make the lucrative switch from their own milk to a formula.** Such practices still go on around the world despite consumer boycotts and protests, but the laws in the UK have been tightened and, although not without loopholes, are increasingly effective.

A SHORT HISTORY OF BREASTFEEDING

Around the 17th century, before the Industrial Revolution, we know that in this country one of the balancing factors in a stable community was women's ability to breastfeed babies for up to three years. Then, age ranges between children were well spaced out and the economic impact of the baby on the family was spread over a wider time frame. The babies were better able to fight infections. The mothers were not constantly drained by continual pregnancy. This vision is now seen as the kind of ideal to which we should all be aspiring again.

Taking people off the land and bringing them to cities, where they lived and worked in overcrowded slums, broke the social cycle and re-organised people's lifestyles. Women went back to work too early in order to make money to pay the rent and so stopped breastfeeding. They fell pregnant again and entered an appalling cycle of deprivation and poverty. The only group of women to whom this did not apply were the very rich and the aristocratic. They were expected to have large numbers of children to carry on the line and demonstrate the fertility of the family. It was specifically because breastfeeding was known to be a contraceptive that such women gave their babies to wet nurses. They were anxious to conceive again. Women who did not feed their own babies were supposedly of good breeding – in reality they were as much victims of their circumstances as their less well-off sisters.

4 Practical Reasons to
Breastfeed
• •

Medical evidence, while not overwhelmingly decisive, points clearly to the facts that breastfeeding is likely to be protective against allergies and breast cancer. There are also fewer cot deaths among breastfed babies than bottle-fed babies.

1 Some studies suggest that physical growth may be slower – in weight terms – for breastfed babies, but without any harm being done. The babies just catch up more strongly later. Other tests suggest the mental powers may be more agile.

2 Breast milk gives babies a greater natural resistance to infection, especially gastro-intestinal infection. Even in the UK it is estimated that a bottle-fed baby is 10 times more likely to suffer gastro-infection. In the third world UNICEF has estimated a child is 25 times more likely to suffer gastro-infections if it is bottle-fed. In poor conditions infections of the stomach which lead to diarhoea and dehydration are a common cause of children dying.

3 Breastfeeding is practical. The milk is at the right temperature. There is no equipment to sterilise. It is free. And the baby will help to use up much of the extra fat put on in pregnancy. Breastfed babies tend to take in less air when they are suckling and therefore are less likely to get wind.

4 The emotional bonding of breastfeeding gives both mother and baby a unique, shared and valuable time together, one that cannot be repeated later.

The history of
formula milks

The first artificial formula was credited to Justus von Liebig around 1860, and was a concoction of wheat, cow's milk, malt flour and bicarbonate of potash. Subsequently, he added pea flour to create a dried version.

It was Henri Nestlé, a German mustard and oil lamp dealer, who first saw that his philanthropy towards women who did not or could not breastfeed, might also be a source of profit. The price of meat was falling and many farmers were being forced to keep their herds on dairying. With their milk, Mr Nestlé launched Farinée Lactée.

At the turn of the century, colonial settlers saw dried milk powder as a way to relieve famine and malnutrition. That it had a commercial benefit sat equally happily. On the strength of these ideals Nestlé became one of the largest food companies in the world.

The basic recipe for formula milk has changed twice this century. The first types used butter fat but, around 1915, it was recognised by the American company (now called SMA) that vegetable fats and other formulations would be closer to breast milk, and also cheaper. The list of fats added to formulas is a rather unnerving agenda from coconut oil to beef tallow to fish oil. The second breakthrough, nearly twenty years later, was to recognise that the composition of breast milk changed. By splitting the whey and the casein content of cow's milk, two different kinds of milk could be sold, each of which mirrored breast milk more accurately at different stages of the baby's development. The idea of follow on-formulas is quite new and allows more vitamins and minerals to be added.

HOW POPULAR ARE FORMULA MILKS & FOLLOW-ON MILKS?

Milk is still the largest single sector of the baby food market – and sales are rising. More mothers are using follow-on milks instead of going over to traditional cow's milk because of the well-advertised message that cow's milk is an imbalanced food for babies and because more mothers are returning to work earlier. The market was worth £139 million in 1992 – up £46 million on 1988.

What is wrong with *formula milk?*

There is nothing wrong with formula milk. It does not have the medical qualities of breast milk that offer the baby the mother's own immune system, nor does it offer the basic intimate opportunity for bonding. It is also sometimes argued that formula milk sets up a poor acid/alkali balance in the gut which discourages the growth of beneficial antibodies. But millions of people were raised on it and most of us would be hard pressed to tell who was and who wasn't.

The major pitfalls of formula milks have been in terms of money and usage. Money, because formula is expensive – especially when it has been marketed in third world countries to mothers who can never hope to afford it and who should always have been advised to breastfeed in the first place. The

---

THE BIGGEST CONSUMER CAMPAIGN IN THE WORLD

The campaign against Nestlé and other formula milk companies has been one of the biggest consumer causes of the century. Famous brands like Nescafé have been boycotted. Nestlé does not sell formula milk in this country, but controls something like half the world market in formula milk. It gives books on baby care to new mothers which carry adverts for formula milk, gives desk pads to doctors advertising the merits of formula milk, and gives doctors free cruises for conferences.

Nestlé actually won the libel case that launched the consumer campaign. It argued that publication of a book in Switzerland on the impact of its policies in the Third World defamed its good name. The judge upheld this claim, but went on to say 'if the complainant [Nestlé] wants to be spared the accusation of immoral and unethical conduct, he will have to change advertising practises'. In one of the great public relations gaffes of all times, the then M.D. refused to do so.

In 1975 'The Bottle Babies', a film by Peter Kreig, illustrated the full horror of what baby formulas can mean in the Third World. Within 24 hours of its screening, action groups had formed across America. In 1977 the first boycott of Nestlé products began. This was briefly suspended when the company said that it would change its policy, but was reintroduced as soon as it became plain that it was still not conforming with WHO/UNICEF guidelines.

formula companies compounded this sin by offering inducements to doctors and health workers to get mothers to stop breastfeeding. This policy, now publicly castigated by organisations as various as the World Health Organisation (WHO) and United Nation's Children's Fund (UNICEF), who originally condoned it, has made them both the richest food companies in the world and also the most despised. It is not overly cynical to conclude that the companies judged that as a consumer pressure group young families were unlikely to be fully committed campaigners and might well lose interest once their children had grown out of the issue. The word-wide boycott against Nestlé products is still active (though Nestlé does not sell formula milks in this country) in protest against the company's unapologetic policy in the Third World.

The second charge is that these companies allowed mothers to move over to dried formula milks in areas where the water supply was potentially dangerous and, as a result, millions of children died from diarrorhea and malnutrition. The women, meanwhile, were locked into a cycle of births that was unhindered by the contraception of breastfeeding and bore increasing numbers of children into misery. The cycle is as evident in this country still as in the Third World, although with less devastating results thanks mainly to our care systems.

HOW MUCH?

The cost of feeding a baby on formula milks for six months, based on the manufacturer's recommendations, is about £190.

HOW MANY MOTHERS BREASTFEED?

Research shows that older mothers are more likely to breastfeed than younger mothers. Only 35% of women under 21 breastfeed their babies but, by 30, more than 7 out of 10 preferred to breastfeed. After six months only 1% of women under 21 were still breastfeeding while 44% of women over 35 were still breastfeeding. Some 70% of women chose to breastfeed their first child but only 59% the second, although these women tended to go on breastfeeding longer. The American surgeon general has set targets for the USA of 75% of all mothers breastfeeding by the year 2000, and 50% carrying on for six months after birth.

CAMPAIGN FOR **A**CTION

IBFAN – the International Baby Food Action Network – still actively monitors the activities of companies across the world. It reports continued abuse of health guidelines: companies selling products with foreign language labelling, inducements for doctors, adverts suggesting that formula-fed babies grow bigger than breastfed ones and the idealising of bottle-fed baby images. These factors encourage the continuing fall in numbers of mothers breastfeeding, especially in countries like Brazil.

What we *think now*

The Red Cross specifically rules against giving out supplies of infant formula milks to mothers in emergency zones. It follows that, even in the direst famine and civil war, formula milk is not a solution and that, whatever else is going on in the world, breastfeeding comes first.

Even if the mother is malnourished herself, breastfeeding is still the best route for both mother and baby, and may well save both their lives.

In 1981 WHO and UNICEF issued a code on selling breast milk substitutes. The code was designed to stop mis-information and the inducements to health workers to persuade women to take up alternatives to breastfeeding.

The stringency of the code underlines just how deeply the formula milk companies were, and in some cases still are,

THE MAIN POINTS OF WHO/UNICEF CODE ON BREAST MILK SUBSTITUTES

❖ **Milk formulas** should not be advertised.
❖ **There should be** no free samples.
❖ **Health workers must not** promote these products.
❖ **Salesmen should not** sell direct to mothers.
❖ **Health workers should refuse** all gifts and inducements.
❖ **Stop idealised photographs** of bottle-feeding babies and accompanying health messages, particularly on labels.
❖ **Information to health workers** must be factual.
❖ **All information on milk substitutes** must include reference to the superior nature of breastfeeding and a warning on the costs and potential dangers of using substitutes.

entwined with the medical profession. They handed out research grants and helped to finance clinics, thereby meeting little resistance from many doctors who only had to hand out the formula...or not even that, just not stop someone else doing it. The initial arrogance that at least if a mother got her feeding supplies from the clinic and the chemist then the baby's food would be safe has been fully discredited.

The issue is not over today. Many of the WHO/UNICEF guidelines are still being ignored, especially in southern countries. The executive director of UNICEF, James P Grant, wrote a personal letter to doctors last year (1994) warning that 'substantial quantities of free infant formula are still routinely distributed through the hospitals and doctors offices of the '90s. Manufacturers regularly provide free and low cost bulk supplies.'

Britain and the EC have fallen roughly, if reluctantly, behind the guidelines, although advertising to health professionals is still allowed, provided it is only of a factual nature. This is one area where politics and commerce overlap. While the EC has a milk lake, it is hardly anxious to advocate an alternative, better, cheaper source of nourishment for babies – mother's milk.

THE INNOCENTI DECLARATION

The nutritional and social aspirations of WHO are documented in this declaration to which all countries are invited to subscribe. It declares:

'As a global goal for optimal maternal and child health nutrition, all women should be enabled to practise exclusive breast-feeding and all infants should be fed exclusively on breast milk from birth to 4-6 months of age. Thereafter, children should continue to breastfeed, while receiving appropriate and adequate complementary foods, for up to two years of age or beyond. This child feeding ideal is to be achieved by creating an appropriate environment of awareness and support so that women can breastfeed in this manner....'

The advice is very specific: 'During the first 4-6 months of life no other food or liquid than breast milk, not even water, is required.' It rejects even the use of water as a drink, or herbal drinks as pain soothers. The WHO view is that most reasons for not staying with breast milk are 'subjective'.

Suppose you can't or *don't want to?*

Not all mothers want to breastfeed, some cannot or there may be special circumstances – perhaps the baby is premature or twins are born (although most women could feed twins). Statistically this dilemma only faces a small number of women. To read the brochures published by formula milk manufacturers you might believe that breastfeeding is immensely difficult and challenging to all. The glossy literature exudes sympathy – so much so that it is almost tempting to pack in the breastfeeding and win the approval. If I sound unsympathetic, then it is only because this book ought to redress the balance.

Some women cannot breastfeed happily. Their milk is just not rich enough. Studies in America suggest as many as 1 in 20 women may not give her baby sufficient nutrients in her milk and should supplement it with an artificial milk. Without it, the babies can get dehydrated – a syndrome known as the Yuppie Famine. They are, quite literally, starving. Here the risk is much smaller. Health visitors are trained to spot the signs. Supplementing the breast milk with formula is another issue.

How Much Milk do Babies Drink ?

A baby drinks about 150ml of milk every 24 hours for every kilogram it weighs. A 4 kg baby needs about 600ml a day, spread out usually through five feeds. Elizabeth Morse in **My Child Won't Eat** (Penguin) declares speculatively that: 'if a child grew at the same rate as in the first year, he would be 29 metres tall and weigh 200 tonnes by the age of 10'.

The Stool Check

It may seem strange to include a section on baby's stools but there is no surer way of knowing that your baby is getting the right food than checking his nappy. Different babies will have different stools depending on what they are eating. At first a new baby being breastfed may have several dirty nappies in a day, although they will only have small stains because the milk is so well digested. After about a month the stools will become less frequent. Several days can even pass without a dirty nappy.

Breastfed babies will often pass greeny yellow or mustardy stools. Bottle-fed babies tend to pass one motion a day which is usually much firmer and normally greenish-yellow.

The instinct
to suckle

Lightly brush a baby's cheek and he will instinctively turn to suckle, seeking out a nipple, teat, or finger. This instinct is at its strongest just after birth but carries on until about six months. Young babies cannot take solids because the act of suckling actually repels the food out of their mouths.

By about five months the head muscles are strong enough for the baby to turn away from the breast or served-up foods. Over the next month he will be able to start making his jaw move round. This is the first sign that chewing is possible.

Bottles are easier for babies to drink from and lazy babies may well prefer a bottle because they do not have to suckle and work for their dinner. Formula milks used to be mixed in with cereals, but there was suspicion of a link with coeliac disease, in which the babies' intestines were irritated by the gluten in the wheat. Nowadays, wheat-based products are not usually recommended before eight months.

ALLERGIES

Around 7.5% of babies show some allergic reaction to cow's milk products. The alternative is products made from soya milk. Three out of four of those sold are prescribed by doctors. Most babies will grow out of their allergy by the time they are about two years. There is no clear answer as to why they react to milk, although allergies appear to run in families.

COW & GATE INFASOY is a formulated soya milk product for babies who can't drink milk. It is available on prescription.

FARLEY'S soy version is based on glucose syrup and, as well as being 'acceptable to babies from birth', is also suggested as an alternative to milk in cooking for children and grown ups.

SMA produces WYSOY, designed specifically for babies with allergies to lactose or sucrose, or who have galactosaemia or coeliac disease. Compared to the competition, the composition is stronger in minerals of calcium, phosphorus and magnesium and also in the vitamins K, B1, B2 and niacin.

First
formula milks

The first formula milks rely on the watery part of the milk – the whey – to reduce the protein level. The ratio is similar to breast milk, with 60% whey as against 40% casein.

Cow & Gate

Premium claims to be 'the next best thing to breast milk' according to its publicity, although other companies claim their products are even closer. The composition closely follows that of breast milk. The protein is both casein, from the curds, and whey, the fat is 95% vegetable oil and the carbohydrate is lactose, the natural milk sugar. A 900g tin will make 10 pints and would last a week of 6oz feeds 5 times a day. It can be fed to a baby for up to a year. Made-up bottles will keep in the fridge for 24 hours at 4°C. They should not be kept for more than an hour out of the fridge. Made-up milks will not freeze well because the milk tends to separate. The tins are recyclable.

Farley's

First Milk is designed for weaning and is mostly demineralised whey milk, vegetable oils and lactose. Farley's produce three milks and used to call them Oster (from the Latin for bones) but has dropped the name.

10 STEPS TO USING INFANT FORMULAS

1 Check the 'best before' date
2 Wash your hands
3 Be accurate in measuring the powder
4 Measure the water first
5 Use the scoop provided
6 Don't use the scoop to measure the water
7 Don't add any more than recommended – too much or too little will just upset the balance of your baby's diet
8 Don't heap the spoon but level it off with a knife
9 Close the tin or bag properly so it keeps longer
10 Store the formula in a cool, dry place

Sainsbury's

First Menu First Stage Milk, 'recommended from birth and when changing from breast milk', contains 23 different vitamins and minerals. It advertises its iron supplements and low sodium levels. It uses skimmed and whole milk, with some lactose.

SMA

Gold is designed as the transfer product from breast with a casein to whey ratio of 40:60. SMA claims to be the market leader in formulas with its two brands – Gold and White.

> **LOOK OUT FOR SUGAR**
>
> Formula milks are not free of sugar, and the same dangers are as implicit as they are in sugared baby drinks. Soya products are often sweetened. Follow-on products – SMA Progress, Farley, and two Boots products – have sugars.

Second *Milks*

As a baby grows so does his appetite and the second generation of infant formulas swap the ratio round of whey and casein so that it is the same as in cow's milk – 80% casein as against only 20% whey.

Cow & Gate

Plus is for hungrier babies. The proportion of casein is higher than the more watery whey, unlike in Premium. It is designed mainly to satsify babies while they are learning to eat solids.

Farley's

Second Milk, unlike their first milk, has maltodextrin. The literature says it is 'suitable from birth' but only in special cases.

Sainsbury's

First Menu Second Stage Milk leaves out the demineralised whey and the magnesium found in the First Milk, but has a similar cocktail of vitamins and minerals.

SMA

White is for the 'hungrier baby', with a ratio of 80:20 in favour of casein. The casein-based milk will take longer to pass through the baby's digestive system. It is sold both as a powder and as a liquid in tetrapaks, convenient but more expensive.

Follow-on *milks*

These are the dynamic growth area in the market place. Follow-on milks can be used from six months up to two years and are already established in Europe, where they account for as much as 40% of baby milk product sales. By six months, a baby might be drinking a pint of milk a day.

Boots

Plain and **Strawberry Follow-on** formula use skimmed milks. Both are reinforced with 14 vitamins, but also vegetable oils, lactose, maltodextrin and anonymous 'flavouring'. Until recently Boots left milks alone until this high profit, low contentious stage.

Cow & Gate

Step-Up is as an alternative to cow's milk for older babies, usually recommended for babies of six months to a year. It has extra iron and vitamins A, C and D. Cow & Gate suggests it is a better milk than cow's milk until two years. Made-up, it will keep in the fridge for 24 hours.

Farley's

Follow-on Milk uses whole milk rather than just skimmed and has no maltodextrin. There is also a strawberry version, which includes maltodextrin and also lactose and fructose to make it sweet. These are suitable for babies up to two years old.

Sainsbury's

First Menu Follow-On claims to be suitable for babies from six to 24 months. It is mostly whole milk, with some demineralised whey and also maltodextrin. The formula includes 23 added vitamins and minerals. There is a banana version which claims to be sucrose-free but contains fructose (in place of maltodextrin) although the total sugars are not shown.

SMA

Progress, designed for babies of six months to two years, makes great play of its iron content, which SMA claims is the highest on the market, although it is actually identical to Cow & Gate's Step-Up. The vitamin content is notably swayed towards the maximum levels of vitamins E, K, B1, Niacin and C compared to other products.

The first
foods

Weaning comes from the old English word 'wenian' meaning to accustom. This is probably just as meaningful for a mother as for the baby. The baby will instinctively develop an interest in textures, more sustaining foods than just milk, and be excited by new flavours.

Weaning also marks the point where a mother starts to re-assert her own individuality and relationship with the outside world. She is not going to breastfeed forever. There is no set time or cast iron schedule for introducing a baby to solid foods. When either mother or baby, or both, feel the time is right, then it is right. Baby foods declare themselves from three months, but there is no harm in beginning to wean at six months.

Weaning is a gradual process, taking place over a few months. Usually the milk stops being enough on its own to satisfy a growing baby, or a mother wants to go back to work. Once weaning begins, it is an irreversible process and many of the benefits of breastfeeding disappear. By six months the immune system of most babies will have kicked in and the vital sustenance of breast milk will have done much of its miraculous work.

First *Tastes*

For babies as yet unable to speak, what they eat must be one of the most important ways in which they interact with the world. It is a silent language, but no less communicative than words. The food we give our children says a lot about the kind of world we live in and the things we think are important.

From a baby's perspective it is one of the first opportunities to assert their own individuality and relate to other people.

Babies start with the best food of all, mother's milk, and then have to take a great leap into the amphitheater of eating with the rest of the family. They have to learn the skills and actions to keep up while experiencing these amazing new tastes and textures. It is exciting. It must be.

A baby rejecting food is just as good news as him eating it. He is announcing himself. And to get anywhere in the world in later life he must do it forcefully so that everyone understands. Babies do not like everything. Being able to communicate that is one of the first great decisions a baby can make.

The first taste of a food other than mother's milk is a wonderful introduction to the world a baby is about to explore. The second feed of the day is usually the best time to introduce something new. A tiny amount of puréed food on the tip of a clean, sterilised, plastic spoon just before feeding must be an exciting experience if you have never tasted, say, an apple or a carrot before. Not only is the food new, but taking food off a spoon is completely different to suckling. And suddenly for the baby, whose diet has been wholly liquid, the food has texture! Imagine: it must be like going into a garden for the first time and being confronted by an abundance of new sensations.

Introduce one flavour at a time. If your baby shows no interest in a food, try something else, and come back to that food. By keeping to one food for two or three days, you can monitor any (unlikely) reaction or allergy which might produce sickness, a rash or diarrhoea. The chances of this happening must be more likely with shop-bought baby foods with their mix of different ingredients – however safe and sanitised – than a simple purée of fruit or vegetables that you might share.

WHERE TO BUY BABY FOODS

Not all supermarkets stock baby foods. Some branches of **Somerfield** and of **Marks and Spencer** don't. **Sainsbury's** and **Safeway** have developed their own baby food labels. **Tesco**, **Asda** and **Waitrose** are content to sell the leading brands. Baby specialists **Mothercare** don't stock foods. The major baby food retailers are **Boots** and other chemists.

The spectrum of *flavours*
....

Learning to eat is like learning to read. You need to know the basics before it is possible to string letters into sentences. Over a period of weeks, cover the main areas of flavour – sweet, sour, salty (that is naturally salty – don't add salt to food). There is also the taste, sometimes called umami, which includes the glutamates found in meat extracts, tomatoes and Parmesan. Try not to give in too easily if your baby favours one type of taste to the others. You may never be able to per-suade him to like one food instead of another, but you can introduce different tastes that he can come back to and enjoy later in life.

Ordinary fruits and vegetables have an infinite variety of flavours in themselves. They don't need extra sugar or salt. Commercial manufacturers are happy to introduce natural herbs and seasonings like basil and parsley or cinnamon and vanilla to their products. If they can do it, then you can do it. Bringing in such flavours one at a time can make shopping and cooking considerably more interesting all round. Although the medical advice tends to preach the cautionary note of one step at a time, in practice the choice of foods any baby can eat is enormous as the list of ingredients in commer-cial baby foods (see pages 61–82) illustrates only too well. There is no need to stick to boring old carrot purée.

Shopping List for Feeding

❖ Two plastic spoons – softer and lighter than metal with no
   sharp edges. Share one of the spoons with baby at mealtimes.
❖ Shallow plastic bowl – ordinary plates cool food too quickly
   and are breakable.
❖ Bibs.
❖ Baby mill – to purée, or a good metal sieve to force it through
   with the back of a spoon.
❖ Newspaper – to cover the floor.
   And as they get older...
❖ Bowl with suction pad – so it doesn't fly off the table surface.
❖ Bib with sleeves.

Cooking those *first meals*

First meals are often quite watery, milky purées which allow the baby's body to adapt to absorbing the new and very different forms of minerals and vitamins.

After a week, a baby might be taking two to three teaspoons of purée once a day as well as his usual milk. There is no need to force the pace: a baby will eat in line with his or her hunger. Even at five months, a baby still gets his main source of nourishment from milk, not from solids.

The first foods should be things that you like. They should be simple and pure. Pips and seeds – especially in fruits like strawberries and raspberries – need to be picked out. The natural sweetness of carrots and bananas will appeal to a young palate, but over a period of weeks you may want to bring in a range of different flavours, some more savoury, like marrow perhaps, to make mealtimes more excit-

PERFECT **P**URÉE: **M**ASHED

- Avocado
- Banana
- Peach
- Melon
- Mango

1 Peel the fruit.
2 Mash to a soft purée with the back of a fork.

PERFECT PUREES: COOKED

apple • pear • carrot • potato • swede • turnip • marrow

1 Wash, peel and remove any pips or seeds.
2 Cut into small pieces. Steam or simmer in a small amount of water. Do not add salt or sugar. Cook until the texture is well softened, but not so much that all the nutrients have been destroyed.
3 Strain, keeping back the cooking water.
4 Mash, sieve or liquidise. Mix in a little cooking water so the food is not too solid.
5 Taste and make sure it is not too hot.
6 Sterilise an ice cube tray and freeze what is left.

ing. Avocado is one the prime weaning foods for babies in producing countries, but make sure it is soft and ripe (squeeze the base which should be giving, not the tip as this damages the fruit). Avoid the more acid varieties of apples and acidic fruits like tomatoes for the first few weeks.

Cooked *purées*

Cooked purées are worth freezing (provided you remember to take them out of the freezer the night before). You might cook a mixture of root vegetables – carrots, turnips, swedes and potatoes in one batch, to vary your options through the week. Equally the vegetables could be baked slowly, wrapped in tin foil, which is practical if you have more time at the beginning of the day. Older children and partners may be happy to eat them too, which saves cooking an extra meal.

For a baby, vegetables are cooked when a fork will go through them. After the first few weeks, single vegetable purées can be mixed with each other and with other foods to make meals more interesting and to build up a vocabulary of tastes.

T AKE T EN

10 healthy dishes that all the family can eat (including baby)

1 Porridge
2 Rice pudding
3 Risotto
4 Semolina
5 Macaroni cheese
6 Spaghetti bolognese
7 Vegetable soup
8 Cauliflower cheese
9 Ratatouille
10 Fruit compote

5 RULES FOR FREEZING

1 Keep the freezer at below 0˚ centigrade.
2 Sterilise containers each time they are used.
3 Cover food while cooling with a clean lid or foil.
4 Thaw food thoroughly in the fridge first – especially meat dishes.
5 Reheat food in a sterilised bowl, standing it in a saucepan of boiling water.

First
textures
• •

**The first packet baby foods are invariably based on rice – or
not actually rice but rice flours.**

Whole brown rice has too much fibre for a very young baby
and is not recommended before five months for exactly the
same reasons that it is recommended to you when you are
older. Rice flours can be blended with mother's milk so that
the first taste of the world is a gentle one but a baby's system
is given an introduction to the idea of a thicker texture than
just milk. After a few days the milk and rice flour base can be
made more interesting by adding fruit and vegetable purées.

Milupa

Pure Baby Rice is a first weaning food, recommended for mix-
ing with baby's usual milk and some stewed fruit or mashed
banana. There is also an organic variation under the **Natural
Choice** range.

Cow & Gate

Pure Baby Rice with added B1 (thiamin) is to be mixed in equal
proportion to breast milk. Add the flavours gradually – start
with carrot purée and follow with a mixed vegetable purée.

Farley's

Baby Rice and **Baby Rice with Apple** are sold under the *First
Timers* name. The former is a blend of rice flour, soya flour,
maize flour, yeast, vitamins and minerals, while the latter has
reinforced 'natural flavour'.

Dove's Farm

First Stage Brown Rice Flour is mixed in a ratio of one to five
with breast milk, recommended from five months. Put both in a
pan and bring to a boil, simmer gently for five minutes and
allow to cool. For older babies, the recipe can be varied. Mix
two parts flour to ten parts milk to one part grated vegetables.
Simmer together for seven minutes. Add one part grated cheese,
tahini or tofu. Dove's Farm is an organic milling business.

The real cost of *baby foods*

Mothers are not, so the market researchers claim, overly concerned about the costs of baby foods, rightly being more concerned by quality. Even so, it is interesting – and rather frightening – to see what the mark-up means for family finance.

Farley's suggest that a three to four month old baby might consume 10g of food a day. By five months this will be 20g and by six months and over it will be 30g. For example, Farley's parent company **Heinz** sell a ready-made meal in a jar at 42p for 128g. Supposing this were fed to a three month old baby; by the time he reaches six months you would have spent around £600. This, of course, presumes that the jars are properly re-sealed and kept in the fridge between meals to get the maximum amount from each jar and does not allow for your baby eating anything else. To put this in context, that is the same amount of money, according to the Sainsbury's estimate, that a family of four might live on for three months.

Ready-made baby meals are no better nutritionally than puréed fresh fruit and vegetables with pure rice flour or muesli. The saving in convenience is marginal too.

The rice *rip-off*

Rice flour sells for 99p per kg wholesale. In wholefood shops it can be bought for 75p for 500g. The big manufacturers slap enormous mark-ups on top of that. At our local chemist 100g of baby rice sells for 139p from Cow & Gate and Farley's, while Milupa's baby rice is 165p for 150g. These represent mark-ups of more than 1000 per cent, which is higher than on any other baby foods. Shake the enormous box to test how loose the packet inside is: larger boxes are used to give a false impression of how much you are getting for your money.

WHY NOT GLUTEN?

Most texts preach that the first weaning foods should be gluten-free, although only a few babies are sensitive to gluten. Gluten is found in the main cereals like wheat, rye, oats and barley. Usually the gluten breakfasts, like muesli, are not introduced until five or six months when the baby's constitution is stronger and more adaptable. The packet labelling is usually reliable, although it is often unclear why one product is gluten-free and not another. Rice is commonly used as a first food because it has no gluten content.

Digesting
the rusk

Rusks were originally called Biscottes de Paris and were popular in Holland and Belgium before the Second World War as a normal biscuit famed for their digestibility.

The ingredients – flour, milk, butter and sugar – were similar to those of other biscuits, and only cutting them into fancy shapes and drying them out in a low oven for 3-4 hours distinguished them in any way. There was nothing special about them for babies, but they are held to be good weaning foods – good because they are finger-foods, have texture, are safe and, potentially, can actually taste of something. They can also be broken up and mixed with mother's milk as a first food.

Rusks have evolved into being a baked variation of baby food, breads without the yeast, and most are fortified with vitamins and minerals. Apart from being rather dubious in themselves for young children, some of the flavours are bizarre. Neither orange nor apricot bread has ever been especially popular with adults, so why have orange or apricot rusks? The main difference between the brands is shape.

Farley's

Original uses wheat flour, sugar, vegetable oil, calcium carbonate, emulsifier (E471), iron, niacin, riboflavin, thiamin. The taste, as you would expect, is quite biscuity. It is pleasant, but rather sugary.

Low-sugar variety uses half the sugar and contains wheat, maize and malt flours, and demineralised whey powder. Farley's other two flavours are **Banana** and **Orange**. Farley's four kinds of rusk are baked in large flying-saucer rounds.

Boots

Ruskmen are cutely baked in shapes resembling gingerbread men. The flavoured versions have high percentages of extenders such as cornflour, glucose syrup, soya flour, whey powders, emulsifiers and hydrogenated vegetable fats. To compensate, they are injected with the standard Boots serum of 19 vitamins.

Jacobs

LIGA brand proclaims that is it gluten- and milk protein-free. They are based on maize and potato starch and extended with soya flour and rice starch. The glucose syrup and sugar level is still prominent, but the taste is not as strong as other brands. Quite a mealy biscuit cut into neat little squares.

Bickiepeggs

Bickiepeggs, a tweely named variation of the rusk, created in 1925 by Dr Harry Campbell as an aid to teething. The biscuits are hard, brown, malt-flavoured and have a hole at one end for stringing the biscuit to a baby's clothes. They are made simply of wheat flour and wheat germ, and they should not be sucked for more than 20 minutes.

Inside the packets are weird and whacky offers for things such as 'Forehead Thermometer' and 'Too Hot' warning labels. They cost about 9p each. The manufacturers claim that Bickiepeggs 'have been giving babies and parents a good night's sleep for over 60 years'. From six months.

Second
tastes

· ·

The tradition of infant foods has been to solid safe and sensible images of grandmother cooking garden vegetables or farmhouse vegetable and beef broths, all of which seems a far cry from tipping out a packet of flakes with breast milk, milk or boiled water.

There are two main types of baby food products available – the packets of dried flakes, which are convenient and will keep, and the jars of ready-made purées which are expensive but useful, especially if you are busy, fed up with cooking or just want to give your baby a taste of something new and different. As a rule of thumb, the jars tend to have less ingredients than the dried foods. And, strangely, the more a baby food is made to sound grown-up – say steak and kidney hot pot – the longer the list of other ingredients seems to be. Names bear very little relationship to what is on the packet. They may call it macaroni cheese but it probably doesn't look like any macaroni cheese you have ever seen. Quite what rice, potato and maltodextrin are doing in cauliflower cheese is anybody's guess. What they are not doing is improving the quality of either the cauliflower or the cheese, which might have been a very acceptable dinner in themselves.

Joining in at *mealtimes*

Most manufactured baby foods for recently weaned babies are famously dull and gruel-like, although some of the breakfast cereals and desserts are worth sharing, if only to show moral support. Sweet baby foods are the closest to grown-up food and often quite palatable.

Sharing food is important. If a mother thinks the food is pretty horrible, it is only a matter of time before a baby picks up on that. And in the years to come you may regret passing on your dislikes because babies have dislikes too. If you think it is horrible muck, then don't serve it. If you can't find anything to feed him, purée what you are going to eat yourself.

Baby foods
what's in them?

Manufactured baby foods split into three camps: the chemists or drug companies, the mainstream market, and the organic ranges.

Firstly, there are the foods produced by chemists or drug companies, which tend to sell more on the health-giving properties they have put in – vitamins and minerals in various cocktails for which great powers are claimed or suggested. Ironically, although food companies cannot by law claim their foods to be good for you, there is nothing to stop a chemical company selling its potions as if they were foods.

Secondly, there is the mainstream market which does not have very much to say for itself except in some cases some worryingly long lists of ingredients – especially in dried foods.

In the last few years there has been a dynamic arrival of organic ranges which ask basic questions about everything else on the market. Not just because the cereals tend to be organic – though often only one or two ingredients are, in fact, organic – but because these ranges contain none of the additives that prop up mainstream baby foods. If they are not needed in organic baby foods, why are they included in mainstream foods?

HIDDEN SUGARS

While the companies were making great mileage out of their concern for minority issues like gluten, the rest of the world was more worried about the levels of sugar being pumped into those foods which affect all babies. There has been some reaction in foods as well as drinks.

Milupa was quick to point out that their infant range of yoghurts contains less sugar than comparable yoghurt ranges; the foods in its Natural Choice range are sugar-free or have low sugar levels; and it claims its Rice Pudding has the least sugar of any product on the market. **Heinz** had a rather better argument ready with its Pure Fruit Purées.

The success, or at least the threat of the success, of the small Dorset based **Baby Organix** has led to most of the big multinationals bringing in organic ranges. In **Milupa's** case the extraordinary thing is that the mainstream foods get a dose of 12 vitamins but these are left out of the organic **Natural Choice Range**. Is this just parsimony, or a tacit acceptance that the supplements are unnecessary?

Baby food may well be an area where the organic cause has begun to make some serious inroads into the culture of the food industry – much more so than other areas. For baby foods, the term organic has come to mean rather more than being free of pesticides. It is almost a slogan for purity.

The return to simplicity in the organic ranges like **Baby Organix** might also encourage you to cook your own baby foods rather than paying considerably more for what is essentially just a purée of, say, carrots. The organic movement has really shown up commercial baby foods as the emperor's new clothes – lots of ingredients and nice packaging for no particular benefit to the baby or mother.

Exploiting the *health message*

The long lists in adverts, brochures and on labels of what is in, and what is not in, some baby foods – gluten-free, egg-free, no milk, no artificial flavourings – are more about the industry's paranoia than necessarily about a baby's health.

There does seem to be a collusion among multinational companies to encourage the idea that there *might* be something wrong with your baby to encourage a deeper reliance on their brands, vitamin supplements, and supposed expertise in infant nutrition and on their wrongly perceived links with the medical profession. Many of the promotional claims are just nonsense: that honeyed semolina pudding is suitable for vegetarians is hardly front page news, nor is the fact that sunripe banana has no egg in it. The pedalling of angst wrapped as concern is as common as it is immoral. In reality, health concerns about, say, gluten are only valid for a small number of babies, all of whom will be getting direct dietary advice from their doctor.

Ask your doctor if you are worried about your baby's health and diet. Many baby food companies have supposedly friendly advice lines offering detailed help on bringing up babies but they are not much more than fronts for public relations exercises, and their glossy, feckless literature.

Up and down the *aisles*

• •

A full breakdown of the foods sold for babies from 3 months and older.

✔ *better than average*

✗ *worse than average*

BREAKFASTS

Baby Organix

✔ A good range of pure foods based on whole cereals and dried fruits, milled finely enough for young babies. They are actually edible for adults, probably because they don't have lots of extra ingredients. The banana porridge tastes like sherbert.

	Additional ingredients
Banana porridge	Apples.
Baby rice with apples	Nothing else.
Oat cereal with apple and strawberry	Also banana.

Boots

Boots has a big range of own label baby foods although it is not available at every shop and the products tend to change. The **First Harvest** label is for the organic range.

READY TO SERVE

Fruit and Yoghurt Cereal	Mostly orange, apple, black cherry and raspberry juices.
✗ **Mixed Cereal**	Barley, wheat, rye, oats, rice with added sugar.
Malted Rusk	Mostly skimmed milk and sugar with malted barley.
✔ **First Harvest Muesli**	Mostly oats with bananas, apples, apricots and honey.
✔ **First Harvest Muesli with Dates**	Also apples and bananas, and millet, hazelnuts and wheatgerm.

Cow & Gate

Cow & Gate has lost some of its ground to its trendy new off-spring, the oddly named **Olvarit** (see page 64), but survives with a small range of eleven packet meals at this age range. All the breakfasts have added sugar.

	Additional ingredients
Rice Cereal	Includes milk and added sugar.
Creamed Porridge	Added sugar and some gluten.
Mixed Cereal	Includes gluten, milk, soy and added sugar.
Banana Cereal	Added sugar and milk.

Familia

A Swiss company that sells muesli through health food shops, but is conspicuously better value than main lines with a standard box weighing 340g, in comparison to the normal 100g box used by better known manufacturers.

✔ **Muesli Baby Food** — Oats, whole wheat, whole rye, millet, dates, dried apples, bananas, almonds and wheatgerm; no added sugar.

Farley's

✗ The Farley's range includes an extraordinary number of different ingredients with sugar and maltodextrin figuring prominently as the second and third ingredient in most products.

✗ **Fruit and Yoghurt** — A stunning 25 ingredients with the fruits reinforced by extracts. Also includes exotic fruits like bilberries and elderberries (presumably for colour). High levels of sugar and maltodextrin.

✗ **Muesli** — The 23 ingredients include oats, wheat, soya and malted barley supported by maltodextrin and sugar; also exotic ingredients like maple and fenugreek.

✗ Oats and Apples — Has 21 ingredients – again with maltodextrin and sugar prominent.

✗ Banana — Wheat, oats, maize, barley and rye – the banana is, in fact, the tenth ingredient and is supported by banana extract.

Oats and Orange — Oats, wheat and soya; the colour comes from carrot as well as orange.

✗ Apricot and Muesli — Predominantly maltodextrin.

✗ Summer Fruits — More sugar than fruit.

✗ Creamy Oat Porridge — More maltodextrin and sugar than milk.

Heinz

The Heinz baby range is notable for the number of ingredients used in the products – between 11 and 17. These include vitamin C and iron. There is no added sugar in any of the fruit breakfasts, only the porridge.

Creamed Porridge — Made with skimmed milk, added vanilla and iron.

✔ Mixed Fruit Muesli — Mainly apple juice, pineapple, orange juice and bananas with some oats and wheat in yoghurt.

Apple and Banana Cereal — Apple juice and apples, bananas and lemon juice.

Apple and Apricot Cereal — Rice flour, oat flour and wheat flakes and cornflour.

Tropical Fruit Cereal — Mainly pineapple, apple, melon and orange juices, and apples.

Olvarit

Olvarit is the trendy name for **Cow & Gate's** ready cooked range. Meals should always be served in a dish, not straight out of the jar. Any leftover will keep for 48 hours in the fridge. Freezing affects the texture and is not recommended. The safety button on the top of the jars is a sign that the vacuum is unbroken. If the button is raised or can be moved up and down, the jar may not be safe and should be returned to the manufacturer. The jars are recyclable.

	Additional ingredients
Apple and Banana with Rice	Gluten-free.
Mixed Fruit and Rice Cereal	Gluten-free; mainly fermented milk with pineapple juice.
Creamed Porridge	Gluten left in; has milk and added sugar; classic recipe uses oatflour at this stage which grades up to oats for babies over 7 months.

Milupa

Milupa adds 12 vitamins to most formulations. These are A, D3, E, C, B1, B2, Niacin, B6, Folacin, B12, Biotin and Panthothenic acid. The exception, perhaps oddly, is its organic **Natural Choice** range: there is no added sugar in the Country Harvest Breakfast or the Wheaty Breakfast Cereal. The standard range Milupa breakfasts rely on milk-based thickeners. Most include maltodextrin as well as calcium, vitamin concentrates and iron. There is not much difference in the nutritional values, only in the total sugars, which range from a low of 6g for 7 Cereal to a high of 9.2g for Oat Cereal with Apple.

7 Cereal	Contains 16 ingredients – wheat, oats, barley, rye, millet, rice and maize in skimmed milk; gluten is left in. Also has extenders such as maltodextrin and sucrose. More positively, there is iron as well as vanilla and cinnamon.

Sunshine Orange	Rice and maize in skimmed milk with lemon, orange and passion fruit; contains iron but also sucrose and dextrose.
Oat Cereal with Apple	Has gluten and the highest sugar levels in the Milupa range.
Sunripe Banana	High in sugar.
Wheat Cereal with Honey	In fact, semolina; has gluten.
Porridge Oats	Also contains skimmed milk, vegetable fat, maltodextrin, sucrose, calcium, vitamin supplement and iron; has gluten.
Harvest Muesli	Uses apple, wheat flakes, oat flakes, hazelnuts, honey and raisins; has gluten; also contains maltodextrin and high sugar levels.
Fruit with Yoghurt	Rice and maize with fruit powder – banana, orange, papaya and guava, but less than levels of sucrose an dextrose.

Milupa: Natural Choice

Milupa's organic range. There is no addition of 12 vitamins as in the standard range. Sugar levels are considerably lower than in other Milupa breakfasts too, at 2.1g and 2.4g compared to 6g in the standard range.

Pure Baby Rice	Only trace sugars.
✔ **Wheaty Breakfast Cereal**	Has gluten.
✔ **Harvest Breakfast**	Wheat, oats, rye, maize, barley, millet and rice; has gluten.
Honeyed Semolina	Sugars at 4.9g still lower than in main-line range; imaginative use of vanilla and cinnamon.

Sainsbury's

The Sainsbury intervention in the market place borrows some of the Boots style medical approach with products containing a mixture of added vitamins and minerals. The instant powders include dairy and flour derivates and compensate for extending ingredients with added vitamins. The sugar levels in the breakfasts are noticeable at around 7%, with packets varying in recommending a three or four months old start. The boast 'high quality ingredients encourage your baby to enjoy...' is a bit tenuous in nutritional terms, although 'a variety of flavours' is genuine. The jars have less ingredients or added minerals but are about twice the price of the packets.

Additional ingredients

JARS

Creamed Porridge — Whole milk, oat flour and sugar only.

Banana and Apple — Fermented milk bulked with wheat starch, cornflour, lemon juice and maize oil.

Pear, Banana and Apricot — Varies from above in containing milk instead of soya.

✔ **Sunshine Fruits** — Fermented whole milk with orange and grape juices, and banana.

INSTANT

✗ **Rice Pudding** — Contains maltodextrin, caster sugar and 13 vitamins and minerals.

✗ **Yoghurt and Fruit** — Also maltodextrin and sugar.

Porridge — Oat flour with maltodextrin, skimmed milk and sugar.

✗ **Banana Cereal** — Includes maltodextrin, dextrose, sugar.

✗ **Muesli** — Oat flour with maltodextrin and sugar.

✗ **Apple and Cereal** — Mostly sugar and rice flour; also 27 other ingredients including a mixture of vitamins and minerals.

DINNERS

Baby Organics

✔ The range is strictly additive free, usually the name covers all the ingredients.

Potato and Cauliflower	More cauliflower than potato.
✔ **Pear and Apple and oats**	Sweetened with honey.
✔ **Summer Carrot Purée**	Just carrots and water.
Garden Vegetables	Carrots, spinach, potatoes, tomatoes, leeks, celery and herbs.
✔ **Apple and Rice**	Sweetened with honey.
Apples and Bananas	As above.

Boots

Boots does one of the largest range of baby foods both as purées in jars and also as dried cereals. Both have a mixed cocktail of 18 vitamins – calcium, vitamin C, iron, niacin, vitamin E, zinc, pantothenic acid, vitamin A, copper, riboflavin, thiamin, vitamin B6, folic acid, iodine, manganese, vitamin K, vitamin D and vitamin B12. They are virtually medicines. The soups include a mixture of only five vitamins. Nearly all the savoury dishes rely on soya oil, a good source of vitamin E, albeit the quantities are fractional. The dried range relies on maltodextrin. Not all the ingredients in the organic range are organic.

JARS

✔ **Apple Purée**	With concentrated juice.
✔ **Mixed Fruit Purée**	Apples, bananas and apricots.
Mixed Vegetable Purée	Water with carrot, potato, spinach, peas and thickener.
Chicken and Tomato Savoury	In rice flour.
Vegetable and Lamb Casserole	Mainly potatoes and carrots.
Cheese and Pasta	With eggs.
Country Vegetable Casserole	Mainly potatoes, carrots and tomatoes.
Vegetable and Meat Casserole	Some beef and ham.

Additional ingredients

DRIED

Celery Cheese — With rice and maltodextrin.

Vegetable Supreme — Carrots, tomatoes, potatoes with rice and maltodextrin.

Cauliflower and Potato Bake — As above.

Vegetable and Steak Dinner — Cauliflower, potatoes, leek, and onions.

READY TO SERVE

Cream of Carrot and Potato Soup — In skimmed milk; with added sugar.

Cream of Leek and Potato — Also butter, cream and spinach.

✔ **Cream of Mixed Vegetables** — Mainly potatoes, carrots, onions.

✗ **Cream of Tomato** — Also maltodextrin and sugar.

FIRST HARVEST (ORGANIC)

Boots has two romantically labelled ranges of supposedly organic wholesome foods. However, given the current discussion of the term 'organic' when related to milk and beef, the term is open to interpretation. In my view, not all the other ingredients are organic.

Vegetables with Beef — Carrots, peas, potatoes.

Chicken Supreme — Parsnips and parsley with wholegrain rice (not organic).

✔ **Chicken Risotto** — Carrots, tomatoes, peas and organic rice.

Farmhouse Ham and Pasta — Organic carrots, tomatoes and onions in noodles.

✔ **Vegetable Risotto** — Organic carrots, broccoli and peas in organic wholegrain rice.

Creamy Country Vegetables — Organic parsnips, potatoes, cauliflower, parsley in (supposedly) organic milk and cream.

MOTHER'S RECIPES RANGE

Mixed Vegetables — Organic carrots, potatoes, cauliflower.

Carrots and Potatoes — Organic.

✔ Carrots and Wholegrain Rice	Organic.
Apple and Carrot Juice	Organic.
Creamed Spinach and Potato	Organic.
✔ Garden Vegetables with Wholegrain	Organic carrots and, innovatively, sweetcorn and fennel.
Vegetables and Chicken	Organic carrots, sweetcorn and potatoes.
Spring Carrots	Organic.
Steak Risotto	Mostly carrots, tomatoes and potatoes; claims organic beef.
Beef Medley	Claims organic beef; and potatoes in rice.

Cow & Gate

Only a small range relying on soya even if not sold as such.

Beef Casserole	Includes soya to bulk out.
Chicken Casserole	As above.
Mixed Vegetables	As above.
Cheese and Tomato	With milk.

Farley's

✗ Farley's might well be re-christened Maltodextrin International. Meals are sold as **Lunch Timers** or **Tea Timers**, although there is no obvious difference between products in the two lines. There is a big effort to make meals seem grown-up but this has led to the introduction of many more ingredients than seem strictly necessary.

Beef Cottage Pie	Potato, carrot, rice flour and maize flour; added vitamins, flavours and extracts.
✗ Chicken Casserole	Potato, carrot, mushroom rice flour and more maltodextrin than chicken.
Spring Vegetables with Lamb	More maize and rice flour than potato, carrot or spinach.
✔ Country Vegetables with Turkey	Conversely more potato, spinach and carrot than rice flour.

	Additional ingredients
Mixed Vegetable Casserole	Peas, potatoes, spinach, carrots and maltodextrin.
Cheese and Vegetable Bake	Rice, maize and, unusually, mustard flours; the cheese is not made with vegetarian rennet.
Cheese and Tomato	Tomato in rice and maize flours with maltodextrin.
Cauliflower Cheese	Rye and maize flours with maltodextrin; vegetarian rennet used in the cheese.
Macaroni Cheese	Rice, maize, durum wheat, soya and mustard colours with maltodextrin; vegetarian rennet used in the cheese.
Spaghetti Bolognese	Tomato with rice, maize, durum wheat and soya flours, maltodextrin and potato; some garlic and basil.

Heinz

The range of dinners is sensibly mainstream with a good choice of ingredients and ideas, a low count of additives, and plenty for vegetarians.

Carrots, Parsnip and Chicken	More potato than chicken.
Vegetables and Beef Casserole	Mostly carrot thickened with rice and wheat flour.
Country Vegetables and Beef	As above without the thickeners.
Creamed Potato and Broccoli	Also swede and cheddar using vegetarian rennet.
✔ **Farmhouse Vegetable Soup**	Carrot, potato, parsnip, sweetcorn, peas in tomato purée and rice flour.
Hawaiian Special with Chicken	The 'Special' is carrot in pineapple juice; also some unexotic swede and haricot beans.

Baked Beans with Bacon	Interesting that Heinz introduces its baked beans with bacon to start; the fibre content may be high for a very young baby.
Lancashire Hotpot	Lamb in lamb stock – though some advice is to stay away from lamb as a first meat.
Spaghetti Bolognese	Uses beef stock.
Tomato and Bean Risotto	Also sweetcorn and mushroom.
Vegetable and Lentil Bake	Carrot, swede, potato, corn, cheddar, soya flour, mushroom and tomato purée all come before the lentils.
Carrot and Lamb with Rosemary	In rice flour.
Vegetables and Chicken	Only carrot and potato.
Cheesy Parsnip Bake	Carrot and potato with parsnip.
Choice Carrots and Peas with Beef	Thickened with rice flour.
Country Beef with Carrots	Thickened with tomato purée.
Country Vegetables and Rice	Carrot, parsnip, cauliflower, onion and swede.
Creamed Vegetable Harvest	Carrot, peas, swede, potato, parsnip in rice flour, with spinach.
Farmhouse Vegetable and Turkey	Carrot, swede, cauliflower with turkey in chicken stock.
Fisherman's Pie	Carrot, potato and unspecified white fish; also egg.
Garden Vegetables with Chicken	Carrot, potato and swede.
Sweetcorn with Chicken	In dried skimmed milk.
Pasta Bolognese	The only difference to the spaghetti is the macaroni flour.
Vegetable Bake with Coriander	Carrots, cauliflower, haricot beans, peas and parsnips in rice.

Heinz Pour-Over Sauces

Pure and not overly stocked with unnecessary ingredients. They are all gluten- and egg-free.

	Additional ingredients
Beef Sauce	Tomato and beef only.
Beef and Vegetable	More tomato and onion than beef; also with mushroom.
Chicken	All chicken except a small amount of tomato.
Creamy Vegetable	Mostly onion and potato mixed in skimmed milk and vegetable stock; the cream is 3%; some carrot and mushroom.
Fruity Tomato	With apple and lemon juices, flour.

Milupa

The infant dinner ranges are egg-free, while soya and maltodextrin are usually used to add bulk. Most of the dinners include a range of vitamin and mineral supplements – calcium carbonate, vitamin concentrate and iron. The range is all dried foods, which is practical and economical to fall back on. However, Milupa might be said to be responsible for the widely held adage that all baby foods are bland. The spices on the label sound exotic – for example, vanilla, pepper and cinnamon – but are normally used so sparingly that their flavours are indiscernable. The difference between Garden Vegetables and Spring Vegetables or even Vegetable Hotpot seems slightly marginal.

Garden Vegetables	Carrot, cauliflower, peas, potatoes, spinach, tomato and celery; uses soya for bulk protein.
Spring Vegetables	Carrot, celery, parsley, leek and peas; also yeast and soya for bulk.
Cauliflower and Creamed Potato	No soya, but maltodextrin.

Vegetable Hotpot	Cauliflower, celery, leek, potato, parsley and peas in skimmed milk; also yeast.
Savoury Vegetable Casserole	Cauliflower, celery, carrot, leek, potato, pea, spinach, onions in semolina and rice; has gluten and wheat.
✗ **Braised Vegetables with Steak**	Rice rather than wheat based as below; includes lecithin and lactose.
✗ **Vegetable and Beef Casserole**	A huge total of 26 ingredients from cauliflower and carrot to lecithin, lactose and nutmeg; has gluten and wheat.
✗ **Vegetables with Golden Chicken**	Carrot, potato, cauliflower, peas, spinach, tomato, celery in rice; chicken is the eleventh ingredient, maltodextrin the tenth.
Vegetable and Chicken Casserole	Cauliflower, celery, potato, leek, parsley and peas, without the rice of above.
Carrot and Tomato	Mainly carrot and tomato; has gluten and wheat.
✗ **Cheese and Apple**	With rice and maltodextrin; the apple is powder reinforced with 'natural flavour'.
✗ **Cauliflower Cheese**	With rice and potato; also maltodextrin.
Cheese and Spinach Mornay	Also carrot, potato, peas and celery with rice and maltodextrin.
Cheese and Tomato	Mostly tomato, carrot, onion pea and leek mixed with rice and maltodextrin; also soya.

Olvarit

Olvarit has avoided adding sugar to all but six of its 30 products. The range is particularly traditional, focusing on one lamb, one beef, one chicken, one rice and one pasta dish for the main courses.

	Additional ingredients
Beef and Vegetable Casserole	Mostly potatoes, carrots, French beans, peas and tomatoes.
Chicken with Peas and Carrots	More peas and carrots than chicken; rice flour to thicken.
Creamed Cauliflower with Lamb	Includes wheat and milk.
Vegetables and Rice	Includes soya for bulk; mostly kidney beans.
Pasta Bolognese	Has gluten, eggs and wheat. Mostly beef stock; also bay, sage and basil.
Carrots and Cauliflower	Added vitamin C; uses apple juice for liquid and rice flour.
Baby Carrots	Added vitamin C; also rice flour.
Cauliflower Cheese	Has wheat and milk.
Ratatouille	Has gluten, wheat, and soya.
Cheese and Vegetable Bake	Has wheat and milk.

Safeway

The first major supermarket to have gone into own label baby foods. Its entry conspicuously sidesteps the more controversial issues of the infant food debate.

Mixed Vegetables with Pasta and Ham	Carrots and tomatoes with egg noodles.
Mixed Vegetables with Chicken	Stock rather than meat, carrot and sweetcorn.
Creamed Vegetables	Parsnips, potato, cauliflower and parsley in milk.

Sainsbury's

The jars are a better buy. The dried range relies heavily on maltodextrin and a wide range of ingredients.

JARS

Carrot and Pea	In skimmed milk with parsley.
Green and White Bean Hotpot	In apple juice with maize starch.
Vegetable and Chicken	Potatoes, carrots, tomato and peas in cornflour; unlike the other dinners in jars, it has no added vitamin C.

INSTANT

✗ **Cheese and Tomato**	Rice flour, tomato and maltodextrin; low in sugar compared to the breakfasts at 2.8%.
✗ **Vegetable Hotpot**	Peas, potatoes, carrots and leeks in maltodextrin with extracts of onion and celery.
✗ **Cauliflower Cheese**	Rice flour, cauliflower and maltodextrin.
✗ **Vegetable and Chicken Casserole**	Potato, spinach and mushrooms in rice flour and maltodextrin; some sage extract.
✗ **Vegetable and Beef Stew**	Tomatoes, potato, carrot and celery in maltodextrin and rice flour; some oregano extract.
✗ **Macaroni Cheese**	Rice flour, maltodextrin, maize flour, skimmed milk powder and vegetable fat.
✗ **Pasta Bolognese**	Tomatoes, maltodextrin, rice flour, maize flour and durum wheat flour.

DESSERTS

From a mother's point of view, sweets are the baby foods you are most likely to enjoy sharing. The move to more pure fruit purées is positive, as is the use of more fromage frais and yoghurts which is preferable to the range of dried additives. However, these yoghurts are so sanitised they tend to lack the beneficial bacteria of the original article so they are not quite as healthy as they might be. Packets of creamed banana hardly seem more convenient than whole bananas.

Boots

The main ranges rely heavily on added sugar and fructose – arguably more justifiable in sweets, but nevertheless a very brash attempt to grab the attention by distorting natural flavours at an early age. The **First Harvest** range dispenses with the sweet approach but makes its money by using rice flour as a cheap ingredient to add bulk.

	Additional ingredients
Mandarin Yoghurt	Whole milk; also orange and apple juice.
Orange and Banana Yoghurt	Whole milk; added sugar.
Strawberry Yoghurt	Whole milk; added sugar.
Chocolate Delight	Mostly water and sugar.
Banana Pudding	Mostly water and sugar.
Peach and Strawberry	More peach, apple and strawberry than sugar.
✗ **Apricot Dream**	Only slightly more apricot than sugar.
Egg Custard	Mostly milk and sugar.

INSTANT

✗ **Creamed Banana**	With dextrose and maltodextrin.
✗ **Fruit Cocktail**	Rice and yoghurt with apple, banana, orange, pear, passion fruit, and apricot; also maltodextrin and fructose.
Chocolate Delight	Semolina and sucrose.

✗ **Strawberry Dream**   Semolina, sucrose and
                           maltodextrin.

FIRST HARVEST
Apple and Banana   Plus vitamin C.
✗ **Apricot Delight**   Mostly apple in rice flour.
Bilberries and Apple Pudding   In rice flour.
Fruit Compote   Pineapple juice, apples,
                      apricot and peach.
Banana, Peach and Apple   With pineapple, orange juice
Delight   and oats.
✔ **Apple and Wholemeal**   With wheat, oats and rye.
Pudding

Farley's

✗ The ingredients listed on Farley's food products bear little
relation to the names on the packets.

Chocolate Pudding   Rice, maize, soya flours; also
                          sugar and maltodextrin –
                          but the cocoa solids are high
                          at 39%.
Banana Custard   Skimmed milk, rice flour,
                       maltodextrin, sugar,
                       cornflour and then banana;
                       no egg.
✗ **Apple Crumble**   Nine ingredients before the
                        apple; rice, wheat, oats,
                        soya, maize, malted barley,
                        malted wheat, sugar and
                        skimmed milk; also
                        maltodextrin.
✗ **Strawberry Yoghurt**   With another 19 ingredients.
✗ **Apricot and Lemon**   With another 16 ingredients.
Yoghurt

Heinz

Heinz sells a range in cans and a larger selection in jars. Some canned products have high sugar levels, although others have good vitamin C levels. The food in jars takes more account of modern ideas on nutrition by using fromage frais and natural fruits for sweetness . ✔ The **Pure Fruit** range is without any additives.

There is another range of frozen foods under the **Baby's Choice** name. The convenience is offset by the impracticality of microwaving them or boiling for 10 minutes, then cooking. The banana and chocolate claims to have 'all the goodness of home-made', but you would have to be a pretty awful cook to produce this.

	Additional ingredients
CANS	
Apricot Custard	With pineapple and lemon juice; added sugar.
Banana Delight	The 'delight' is lemon and orange juices with just 15% vitamin C.
Chocolate Pudding	With cornflour and fat-reduced cocoa.
Creme Caramel	Very sweet with caramelised sugar and glucose syrup.
Egg Custard with Apple	With apple and lemon juice.
Egg Custard with Rice	With added sugar; also in jars.
✔ **Pure Fruit Apple and Banana**	Apple and banana in lemon juice; (also in jars).
✔ **Pure Fruit, Apple and Apricot**	Just apple and apricot.
✔ **Pure Fruit, Just Apple**	Only apple.
✔ **Pure Fruit, Mixed**	Apple, banana, pineapple and black cherry.
✔ **Pure Fruit, Summer Fruit**	Apple, orange juice, banana and pineapple.
Rice Pudding	Thickened with cornflour.
JARS	
Chocolate Dessert	Same as Chocolate Dessert in cans.

Fromage Frais, Apple and Mango	Uses apple juice, not apple.
Fromage Frais, Banana and Blackcurrant	Uses blackcurrant juice.
Fromage Frais, Mandarin	Also orange juice.
Fromage Frais, Pear and Raspberry	Uses pear juice.
Fromage Frais, Pineapple and Melon	Juice of melon and pineapple.
Fromage Frais, Tropical Fruit	Juice from pineapple, orange, passion, kiwi, mango, lime, papaya and banana.
Fruity Juice Dessert, Apple and Banana	Bananas in apple juice.
Fruity Juice Dessert, Apple and Orange	Both juices.
Fruity Juice Dessert, Fruit Salad	Apple, pear, pineapple, and orange juice.
Fruity Juice Dessert, Pear and Cherry	Both juices only.
Pineapple Dessert	Pineapple juice.
Pure Fruit, Apple and Mandarin	Mandarin juice concentrate.
✔ Pure Fruit, Apple and Mango	Just fruit.
✔ Pure Fruit, Apple and Orange	Apple in orange juice.
Yoghurt Dessert, Apple	Juice in low fat yoghurt.
Yoghurt Dessert, Apricot and Apple	Added water.
Yoghurt Dessert, Banana	Low fat yoghurt.
Yoghurt Dessert, Five Fruit	Juices of apple, pineapple, orange and cherry with whole banana.
Yoghurt Dessert, Muesli	Apple and pineapple juice; banana in low fat yoghurt; rolled oats and wheat flakes.
Yoghurt Dessert, Strawberry	Also pear concentrate and black cherry juice for colour.
Yoghurt Dessert, Sunshine Fruit	Same as Five Fruit except for the cherry juice.

Milupa

Milupa is quick to point out that its infant yoghurt range contains less sugar than comparable yoghurt ranges. It was one of the first companies to go over to the new labelling. Compared to similar products from other manufacturers, notably low sugar in the Milupa range are Rice Pudding, Natural Choice Honeyed Semolina Pudding and Strawberry Surprise.

	Additional ingredients
Rice Pudding	Lowest total sugars in the sweet range at 6.3%.
✗ **Semolina with Honey**	Also sucrose and maltodextrin; has gluten and wheat.
Fruit Salad	Apple, pear, banana, orange, apricot with wheat and rice.
Fruit Cocktail	Apple, banana, pineapple and passion fruit in oats and rice; lowest total sugars sweet range at 6.3%.
Pear and Orange	At 9.9% total sugars the highest in the range; uses maize and rice.
✗ **Apricot and Peach**	More rice, maltodextrin and sucrose than fruit; 8.8% total sugars.
Banana and Apple	Mostly skimmed milk, yoghurt and fruit.
✗ **Strawberry Surprise**	More sucrose and fructose than strawberry.

Olvarit

The Olvarit fruit desserts use wheatstarch and cornflour to thicken and, in the more traditional desserts, fermented milks or fromage frais to give a custardy texture, sometimes resorting to vegetable oils to bind them. Most have extra vitamin C added and all the fruit flavours have calcium as well.

Apple and Apricot	Has wheat; added rosehips and vitamin C.
Banana and Blackcurrant	Has wheat and sugar added.
Apple, Banana and Orange	Has wheat; added rosehips and vitamin C.

Summer Fruit Salad	Has wheat; salad is apple, grape, rosehip, red and black currants.
Harvest Fruits	Has wheat; salad is grape juice, pears, plums, apricots and rosehips.
Pear, Pineapple and Orange	Has wheat.
Dutch Apple	Has wheat; with cinnamon.
Hawaiian Fruit Cocktail	Has wheat; contains guava and pineapple.
Traditional Egg Custard	Has eggs, wheat, milk and added sugar.
Banana and Apple Custard	Has wheat and milk; uses fromage frais and cornflour to make custard egg-free.
Strawberry and Raspberry Fool	Uses grape and elderberry juice for colour; cornflour and wheatstarch to thicken.
✗ **Exotic Fruit Surprise**	Includes vegetable oil; the surprise is small amounts of passion fruit and kiwi.
Orange Grape and Banana Delight	Uses vegetable oil.
Traditional Rice Pudding	Added sugar.
Milk Chocolate Dessert	More added sugar than cocoa.
Strawberry and Banana Fool	More grape juice than strawberry; also elderberry and vanilla; fool is fromage frais.
Pineapple and Banana Custard	More grape juice than pineapple or banana; custard from fromage frais.

Safeway

Safeway uses inexpensive rice flour to thicken its products, which are sold strongly on the idea of simple fresh fruit. Some have extra vitamin C added which seems strangely unnecessary for fruit sweets, unless the conclusion is that processed fruits lose their vitamin C content?

Apricot and Apple	Based around rice flour and fortified with vitamin C.

	Additional ingredients
Apple, Peach and Rice	Includes wholegrain rice flour as well as standard rice flour; added vitamin C.
Peach	Peaches in apple juice with rice flour.
Apple and Wild Blueberry	Includes three kinds of apple – the fruit, the juice and the concentrated juice; but whole blueberries rather than the juice of the **Organix** baby food range.

Sainsbury's

A real mish-mash of alternatives. Note the sugar in the Apple and Banana. And the maltodextrin in the fruit salad.

JARS

Apple and Banana	In apple juice and orange thickened with cornflour; 14% sugars.
Chocolate Dessert	Total sugars 14%.
Fruit Salad	Pear, pineapple and apricot in soya protein; sugars 6.7%.
Rice pudding	Total sugars 8.8%.

INSTANT

✗ **Fruit Salad**	Mainly rice flour, sugar and maltodextrin; the fruit is apple, apricot, banana, strawberry and raspberry.

Drinks – the
true story

Drinks are the most controversial area of looking after a baby. The strict advice for mothers with young babies, off the back of the commitment to breastfeeding, is that babies should have only a little boiled and cooled water.

This is rather puritanical, but today's product labels are now self-consciously laden with instructions on brushing babies' teeth, making sure that they drink from beakers not teats, not leaving babies alone with their drinks, and making sure that they are drunk quickly. This is a mea-

---

HIDDEN SUGARS

Sugar is not always what it seems. Sometimes it is labelled under carbohydrate and is not necessarily declared. **Boots** still does this on some drinks. So does **Cadbury's** on chocolate drinks.

Then there are the variations of sugar, such as sucrose, fructose, glucose syrup. Adult fruit drinks that declare themselves as having no added sugar usually use aspartame, which has not been cleared for babies. Some, such as **Kiora**, will use aspartame, glucose syrup and flavourings.

When additives were banned from baby drinks, manufacturers faced a problem of how to preserve their drinks. The answer, ironically, was sugar – or different forms of it – because, as a foodstuff, sugar is not an additive.

But raising the sucrose level makes the product too sweet, and so the answer is to use glucose syrup. **Baby Ribena**, for example, has more glucose than sucrose; although, both are bad for the teeth.

sure of how far makers strayed from medical advice, and they have been falling over themselves to resist regulation. In practical terms, as happened with our own daugher, Grace, after she began to supplement breast milk with a formula, she felt short-changed moving across only to water. The problem with drinks is, simply, sugar. Unlike milk, the residual hidden sugars of drinks stay in contact with babies' teeth and can cause horrific damage. Concentrates of fruit purées also serve to concentrate the natural sugars, even if no sugar is added.

Exploitation

Many drink companies exploit the health angst in unprincipled ways, and many mothers have been persuaded to buy fruit drinks on the basis of the health messages of 'extra vitamin C' or the 'goodness of herbs'. Action Against Sugar, the campaign group, reports that, in many cases, mothers had actually insisted on giving their children fruit drinks because they thought they were doing 'the right thing'. There are outstanding court cases against companies for negligence and culpability, which have been brought by more than 1,000 parents who discovered – the hard way – that drinks high in sugar do damage teeth.

Until the harm that flavoured drinks can do to babies becomes even more widely known, the one thing that might contain their popularity is their very expense. In some cases, flavoured waters – such as those sold by Boots – cost the equivalent of a bottle of table wine and more than a pint of beer.

SUGAR'S BITTER REALITY

Every year in the UK, more than 25,000 children under four have teeth removed under general anaesthetic. The major source of this tooth decay is sugar. Baby drinks have been recognised as a major source of sugar since the late 1960s, but it is only in the last three years that anything has been done. Since the Action and Information on Sugars campaign began in 1992 to highlight the risks, thanks to the determined efforts of its director, Jack Winkler, sales of sugared drinks have fallen by 24 per cent. That consumers are more aware of the harm sugar can cause is evident with the new sugarless baby drinks coming on to the market.

Flavoured waters and
fruity juices

Flavoured waters are new to the market. Although mineral waters are not allowed for babies, flavoured waters are demineralised and flavoured, and so they get round legislation and, possibly, the problem. Evian, Heinz, Cow and Gate and Boots are the main players. Either these are diluted fruit drinks or they are pure waters with a hint of...

Boots

Their **Purified Water With A Hint of...** range can have a teat attached and declares itself sugar-free. But it carries the usual warnings, as if it were a sugar product. This seems odd, because, if it is what it claims to be – water with natural flavourings and no sugar at all, which the Blackcurrant is – these warnings need not apply. Other examples in the range include Lemon and Mint, which have glucose equal to 2.5% sugar. It is not recommended for babies aged less than three months.

Apart from Lemon and Mint, on its labels Boots declares that its range is suitable for babies four weeks and older. This is hardly likely to endear it to breast-feeding campaigners. The labels have different colour-codings; nevertheless, this could be confusing.

The price of the glucose-supported drinks is about 40p for 125ml, which equates to a £2.40 bottle of wine. Their flavourings are exceedingly mild.

The **Ready-diluted range** of fruit juices is in the same colour co-ordinated green. The Apple and Orange contains 11% sugar, and it declares itself as 'ready-to-feed'. Rather feebly, in small type, it suggests that, if it were diluted 2 to 1, it would contain only 3.7% sugar. Yet, although it is only fruit juice and vitamin C, the flavour is strong but natural. The cost is equivalent to a £2.40 bottle of wine. Again, the label suggests adding a Boots teat to the top, which seems to be at odds with other manufacturers' commitment to getting babies and children to drink from beakers and not bottles.

Concentrated Juices from Boots are sugared and use invert syrup and glucose syrup. When diluted 12 to 1, the Blackcurrant with Rosehip contains 3.8% sugar. The label says that this is suitable for babies aged at least three months, but this must be questionable in the light of evidence on the impact of sugars in the diet.

Chocolate Milk Drink for toddlers is in tetrapaks. The drink contains sugar and whole milk, but Boots seeks to justify this with a lavish addition of vitamin mix. In short, this is a vitamin supplement flavoured with chocolate. The flavour is exceedingly sweet, but it is cheaper than the flavoured waters. It works out to about the same price as a £1.50 bottle of wine.

Heinz

Has launched a range of large **Ready-to-Drink Fruit Juices** in 750ml unbreakable bottles. At £1.39, they compare well on price against other made-up drinks. The juice concentrate's natural sugars are about 12% per 125ml drink, and it is fortified with vitamin C. The flavour is well balanced and can even take some dilution. A good, honest product, considering the competition.

Ribena

sells three varieties, each with very different make-ups, but the familiar, lush, dark-blue, health-inspiring, brushed-artwork images of currants make them seem the same – as does the name.

Adult Ribena is made up of water, sucrose, blackcurrant juice, glucose syrup, vitamins, and is coloured with grape skins. is **Baby Ribena** is made up of water, glucose syrup and blackcurrant juice; vitamin C is only added. It carries a warning label: 'This product contains sugars.'

Sugar-free Baby Ribena is sold in tetrapaks at about 25p for 125ml. This drink is only water, natural flavourings of blackcurrant, fennel and vitamin C. The flavour is very different from ordinary Ribena. Were this a 750ml bottle of wine, you would be paying £1.50.

Cow & Gate/Olvarit

Cow & Gate do a range of **Diluted Fruit Drinks** that are 83% water. Even so, the total sugars register at 7.2g. They are expensive, at about 43p for 125ml – or the equivalent of a £2.58 bottle of wine. The concentrated versions cost about one-quarter of this. There are no added sugars but, even so, the natural concentration of sugar in the carbohydrate accounts for 45% sugar in the undiluted form. Vitamin C is added in roughly twice the measure of sugar; so one drink of 125ml provides 90% of the recommended daily intake.

Robinson's

Fruit Juices in tetrapaks are aimed at babies and toddlers. They are mostly just juices with vitamin C; although, the sugar concentrate is about 8%. Compared with the Robinson's adult drinks, they are a lot purer. The Robinson's drinks we bought in Boots cost the equivalent of a £1.35 bottle of wine – cheaper than Boots' own brand. Compare this with supermarkets whose own labels undercut the big brand names.

Sainsbury's

Their range underlines their claim to variety for young people, with innovative **Pear and Peach** as a ready made-up drink, and **Carrot and Orange**, both with the sugars somewhat restrained around 6.5%. The price at £2.34 for the equivalent of a bottle of wine is less modest. On flavour alone they would be worth a ✔. In concentrates there is Apple and Grape, and Apple and Blackcurrant. The only sugars are those naturally found in the fruit. They are better value at under £1 for the equivalent of a bottle of wine. Just adding water increases the price by one and a half times.

Herbal
drinks
••

Herbal drinks have been given to babies in different cultures for even longer than fruit purées and are experiencing a revival because of the move towards less sugar content. The main difference is between the powder and granule forms. This gives the rather odd sensation of picking up a tube of something supposedly full of natural flowers and scents and finding that it resembles either a cocaine white powder or luminescent dog food biscuits.

Boots

✗ **Sugar-free Herbal Drinks** are a new range launched by Boots. Of these, the **Camomile** is a distressing white powder which is, in fact, maltodextrin with camomile flavouring. If you wanted to know what maltodextrin tastes like or feels like on your teeth, then you have it here. The taste is disappointingly medical. It costs about 4.5p a cup.

Milupa

Claims to have led the move to less sugar. It has **Hibiscus, Apple and Raspberry** in violent pink granules, and a variation of that in **Camomile, Hibiscus and Rosehip.** They contain vitamin C and and maltodextrin and are directed at babies more than eight months old. The residual sugars are about 3.6%, and they taste sweet. The price, compared with other drinks, is a bargain at about 3p a drink.

✔ **Milupa Fennel** is completely sugar-free. Inside its blue lid is a surprising Nescafé-type powder that tastes beautifully of licorice but is just extract of fennel. It is nearly as cheap as the older generation of drinks. A camomile variation is expected. Of all the drinks on the market, this is probably the best buy.

Woodwards

The company does a herbal drink that claims to be **Mixed Herbs and Apple,** but in reality is a mix of maltodextrin and sugar, with flavourings of elderberry, hibiscus, rosehip, and an anti-caking agent – no mention of apples. It claims to have

70% less sugar than ordinary granulated products. It is a powder that tastes like off-apple sherbert. The sample I bought had no nutritional analysis. It is made in Germany and is covered with quaint, little drawings of elves, berries and fairies. This gives a good idea of where it comes from – fairyland.

Gripe
water

Gripe water seems to have lost its footing in the market-place. It consists of Terpenless dill-seed oil and sodium bicarbonate. It has no sugar or colourants. The dill is supposed to break down trapped air bubbles, relax cramp in the tummy and create a soothing, warm feeling while the bicarbonate neutralises stomach acid. The taste is strong and long-lastingly oily.

Woodwards

Has been making a variation since 1851. It is not recommended for babies less than one month old. Medical experts say that babies at this age do not suffer from gripe.

Nurse Harvey's Gripe Mixture

Also contains caraway oil and sucrose, both of which influence the flavour strongly, giving it a peculiar taste – like very oily caraway.

Vegetarian *babies*

There is no reason why a baby cannot be brought up as a vegetarian. Many of the commercial baby foods are vegetarian in any case and it is almost as easy to have a meat-free diet as not for the first months of life.

The main difficulty is that meat is the original convenience food and gives many nutrients in one serving. Going without means identifying those same nutrients in other foods. The question of balance, using the full spectrum of different foods, becomes all the more important. (See The Food Pharmacy (page 24) for more detailed information.)

SHOPPING LIST FOR FEEDING

A vegetarian baby should eat food from each of these four categories:

Carbohydrates

- Cereals
- Grains
- Pasta
- Bread
- Rice
- Oats
- Breakfast cereals
- Potatoes

Protein – from beans and pulses such as:

- Peas
- Beans
- Lentils
- Soya products
- Nuts (ground)
- Seeds
- Also eggs (well cooked because of the risk of salmonella)

Vitamins

- Fruit and vegetables

Calories and energy

- Milk
- Cheese
- Yoghurt
- Fromage frais

How healthy are *vegetarian babies*?

As most vegetarians have to think more about their diet, it is possible that they, in fact, eat healthier foods. Using dried pulses which can be soaked, cooked and puréed is both a cheap and highly effective way of feeding a young child. There is just one proviso: most vegetarian diets tend to have very good levels of fibre. A young baby's system is still growing and does not need the kind of bulky pulse dishes grown-ups do.

Vegan *babies*

Calories and energy pose the biggest problem for vegans, who are usually advised to take dietary advice and probably supplements. Obtaining the vitamin B12 is also a problem since, beyond dairy foods, the evidence of where it comes from is unsure. It may well appear in one batch of foods – seaweed and fermented foods like tempeh which were always thought to be good sources – but some research has now questioned this. It may well be that other vitamins are needed to ensure that the body absorbs B12 properly. The area is still poorly understood. The main sources of B12 for vegan babies are:

❖ Soya milks (easily available for babies) ❖ Yeast food

The best answer is to start to supplement normal breast milk with a soya milk alternative to formula.

> ### VEGETARIAN CHEESE
>
> Cheeses that are called vegetarian can use a rennet that is synthesised from a cow's stomach. It is argued that, because the synthesis has created a series of rennets that are not directly from a live animal, they qualify as vegetarian. Peter Cox, a former chairman of the Vegetarian Society, writes in the *Encyclopedia of Vegetarianism* that cheese for this reason should be avoided.

ETHICAL FOODS

The Vegetarian Society symbol of a green sheaf of wheat in a white square is given to foods that conform to the Society's ethical standards. It means the product contains no animal meat or bone stocks, no animal fats, no gelatin, aspic or jelly crystals and no products made from the by-products of slaughterhouses – for example, cheese made with animal rennet, battery or intensively produced farming like eggs.

Stepping up
to solids

· ·

Babies start to show a keen interest in foods, and anything else they might feel like putting in their mouths, around six months. They start to bite the spoon and grasp pieces of food in their hands. Encourage them. It is fun. At last they have discovered the strength in their muscles to move their heads and to begin to chew.

Their mobility in itself accelerates their need for more sustaining foods. Suddenly the whole panoply of sterilising equipment and special foods starts to become less important and everyday foods become possible. Anything that can be eaten with the fingers is a good way of encouraging tactile senses.

Teatime can be completely eaten with the fingers. Slices of bread or even toast – perhaps with a little jam; slices of apple or pear; or florets of cauliflower or sticks of carrot will give a sense of independence and freedom. If he puts too much in his mouth, just hook it out with your little finger.

Stay with your baby while he is eating. Meals should be sociable, happy times – sit down and join in. Don't be tempted to take these precious moments out to finish off a chore. Talk to him and give him plenty of encouragement. Copy his sounds. Take your time. Let him make a mess if he wants to. He is discovering himself and the world around him. Put a sheet of newspaper under the chair to catch the crumbs and anything else that might fall on to the floor.

He will show you the kinds of food he likes. Be guided by him. He might hate rice, porridge and muesli. Explore the larder for things that he might find interesting. Backdrops of mashed potato or mashed lentils can become canvases for interesting, brighter, more varied flavours. Pilchards are cheap. Most children like mashed sardines. Or a little steamed fish. Keep up the habit of serving different fruits, but venture beyond the standard varieties. Try something more exotic, such as kiwi or guava, or apricots or peaches with the stones removed.

Ordinary breakfast cereals, such as Weetabix or Shreddies, offer good routes for exploring the more mealy flavours. As with rusks, they can be easily mashed into soft purées.

Meals should be platforms to bring in textures. Small lumps of food will encourage a baby to chew properly. The main difference between the baby foods at this age is that they should have little pieces of food in them and not just be liquid purées. Eating should become more physical. In nutritional terms there is not much difference between many products at this age and younger. It is the whole foods that matter and bring the new dimensions of the obstacle course of eating whole shreds and shards of vegetable and meats that help development.

From the age of six months, issues like gluten cease to be so important. To give extra energy, many foods switch from skimmed to whole milk powders.

MEAL **T**IMES
6.30–7am Milk.
8–8.30am (an hour after waking) Cereal and toast. Milk.
12.30-1pm Main meal. Dessert. Drink of cooled, boiled water.
5.30-6 pm Tea. Finger-food, such as toast or bread, with fruit or yoghurt. Milk.
Bedtime: Milk.

Up and down the
Aisles
• •

The packaging of these foods suggests that at six months there is some huge watershed, that suddenly baby has grown up. This is mostly a fiction, a premature ejaculation of advertising to hook babies into solids younger than may be necessary. The main difference at this stage is simply that quantities tend to be larger and some of the early taboos, like gluten, have been lifted.

✔ *better than average*

✘ *worse than average*

BREAKFASTS

The sugar levels in breakfast foods are often quite high – in some cases as high as in sweets.

Baby Organix

Baby Organix leaves out more than the others put in. There is a genuine attempt to resist all non-essential ingredients, but this costs a bit more – and the boxes are rather bigger than the packets inside. Nevertheless, Baby Organix has the feel of a first-class wholefood product. Everything can be tasted.

	Additional ingredients
✔ **Apple Muesli**	Wheat, oats, barley, bananas, apples in flakes, almonds and apples.

Milupa

Country Muesli	Oats: wheat, maize, rye, barley, millet, rice with apples, coconuts, and full-cream milk powder. Contains 32 ingredients, including Corn Flakes.

Oranges and passion fruit	Gluten-free and egg-free. Sweet at 8g.

Olvarit

Banana, pineapple and apple muesli	Has wheat; the pineapple is juice.
Mixed fruit muesli	Similar to the above but with small additions of apricots and peaches.
Creamed Porridge	With added sugar.

~

DINNERS

Baby Organix

Most of the range starts at four months. Some interesting exceptions are suggested to start at seven months.

✔ **Mixed cereal with tomatoes and basil**	With oats, wheat, barley.
✔ **Mixed cereal with potatoes and chives**	With oats, wheat, barley.

IN JARS

Apples with cherry juice	With milk, semolina and honey.
✔ **Apple and wild blueberry with muesli**	With wheat, barley, oats and honey.

Boots

The Boots range includes some more grown-up ideas in larger jars and keeps up the vitamin supplements. The **Mother's Recipes** continues the same themes, solidly organic, without the vitamin supplements, and in slightly larger jars.

Cauliflower cheese	With eggs and cream.
Chicken noodles	Mostly carrot but acidulated with lemon juice.
Fish and tomato bake	With potato, lemon and sugar.

	Additional ingredients
Ham and pasta with creamed tomato sauce	Uses wholemeal noodles.
Beef and pasta bake	In apple juice with egg yolk.
Country vegetables	Organic.

INSTANT

✗ **Savoury sweetcorn**	In rice with maltodextrin.
Vegetable and cheese mornay	Celery, carrot and leeks.

Milupa

Milupa doesn't specialise in this age group. It is mostly content to carry on with its range for babies aged three months-plus. It has only four specialised meals, each with an ever-growing list of ingredients that might make you think the company adds vitamin with one arm and extenders with the other.

✗ **Tomato and steak hotpot**	Tomato, potato, pea, onion and carrot in rice, maltodextrin and 18 other components, including bulking soy and milk powders. Has no wheat or gluten.
Harvest vegetables and chicken	Celery, potato, leek, carrot, pea in rice and maltodextrin. Has no wheat or gluten. Uses soya instead.
Pasta bolognese	Has more vegetables – tomatoes, potatoes, carrots, onions, peas, leeks – than the vegetable pasta below. Has gluten, egg and soya.
Italian-style vegetable pasta	Mostly rice and skimmed milk with alphabet pastas. Has gluten and egg.

Olvarit

All the Olvarit main meals contain gluten from the wheatflour used to thicken, except the **Garden Vegetable Risotto**. There is a clever use of herbs, such as the use of thyme and basil – albeit, in tiny quantities – which are good alternatives to sugar and salt. Sold in 200g jars, rather than 150g, and is for three- to six-month olds.

✔ **Vegetables and chicken** — Mostly carrots and potatoes, with chicken stock and parsley.

Chicken and mushroom risotto — Mostly chicken and potato. Sweetened with orange juice.

Cauliflower and tender lamb — Mostly cauliflower and potato. Seasoned with nutmeg.

✔ **Garden vegetable risotto** — Includes soya protein, rosemary, bay and coriander. Gluten-free.

✔ **Cheesy macaroni with leeks** — Seasoned with ginger, thyme and basil.

Pasta bolognese — Made with beef stock. Seasoned with rosemary, thyme, basil.

Beef and vegetable casserole — Good ratio of beef to vegetables.

Cod and tomato special — Mostly vegetables: seasoned with lemon and thyme.

West Country casserole — Mainly kidney beans, beef stock, potatoes and apples.

Country vegetable and egg savoury — Mostly potatoes, beans and peas.

Pasta Italienne — Mostly tomatoes, pork and macaroni cooked in apple juice.

Cauliflower cheese with vegetables — With potatoes, broccoli and carrots.

Ratatouille — Includes pasta and soya.

Highland cheese and vegetable bake — Mostly potatoes, broccoli and carrots.

Vegetables with lentils — Mainly potato and leeks, with skimmed milk.

Safeway

A solidly good homely range that avoids much of the silliness of the bigger brands.

	Additional ingredients
Vegetables with ham and pasta	Mainly meat stock bound with wheat semolina and flour.
Vegetables with chicken	The chicken stock in the three-to-six month range is the smallest ingredient. Now it is the biggest.
Buttered carrots with wholegrain rice	Uses butter and vegetable oil.
✔ **Creamed vegetables with noodles**	Carrots, sweetcorn and smaller bits of cauliflower and fennel.

Sainsbury's

The sugar levels at this stage have been reduced to virtually nothing.

JARS ONLY

Macaroni	Tomatoes, pork and macaroni in apple juice.
✔ **Spaghetti Bolognese**	Pasta, tomatoes, beef stock and beef; total sugars 0.6%; noticeable hints of bay and basil.
Vegetable and Chicken	Carrots, potatoes, tomatoes, chicken in apple juice with wheat flour; very different from the simpler, three months onwards version, 'the first taste of school dinners'.

DESSERTS

Boots

The same determination to appeal to babies as if they were adults is evident, but with sensible combinations of ingredients – perhaps less so in the instant variations.

Banana and yoghurt muesli	Mostly apple.
✔ **William Pear dessert**	Just pears and vitamin C.
✔ **Rice pudding with apple**	Also has some mango.
Crème caramel	Mostly water and sugar.
Creamed rice pudding with nutmeg	Milk, sugar, rice, egg yolk and vitamins.

INSTANT

Forest fruits	Dextrose yoghurt with blackberry, blueberry and raspberry.
✘ **Apricot and passion fruit yoghurt**	More milk, yoghurt, semolina, maltodextrin, sucrose, vegetable fat, and dextrose than fruit.

Milupa

Apple and vanilla sundae	The apple is both in pieces and in powder. Also includes Rice Krispies. 7g total sugar.
Polka dot delight	Mostly skimmed milk, rice, maltodextrin with chocolate. 8.5g total sugar.

Safeway

Apple, banana and yoghurt with mixed cereals	A bumper whack wrapped around mostly wheat, rye and oat flakes.
Mixed fruit with cereal	Apple, pineapple and orange with oats and rice flour.

Sauces

The move to creating pour-over sauces seems to abandon recklessly the principles that companies apply when dealing with milks and other baby foods. The only argument in their favour is that they can be used to disguise more solid items in a sludge that resembles something like the first purée baby foods.

Wetness might be said to be their single virtue. But, as with grown-up foods, the cost of this convenience is huge. In cooking terms, it is also futile. Nine times out of ten, such sauces are more likely to ruin a dish than to improve it. Then there is the matter of how wise it is to introduce an innocent palate to such things as onion powder and modified cornflour.

Heinz

Heinz produces a range of 128g jars, each containing 10-15 ingredients. The five flavours are: **Chicken, Fruity Tomato, Creamy Vegetable, Beef Vegetable** and **Beef Sauce.**

Great claims are made for the quality of Heinz sauces and for their supply of iron; although, only two – Fruity Tomato and Creamy Vegetable – have the added vitamin C that helps the body to make use of it.

The home economy in the promotional brochures suggests that these additions will actually help dishes such as shepherd's pie or spaghetti bolognese. They probably ruin it and bump up the price, not to mention give you another job to do. Comparable adult sauces, it is claimed, 'are often quite unsuitable for babies because of the levels of salt and artificial additives present'. This is quite true, but such sauces are not really suitable for adults, either. Transporting the culture of high value added, nutritionally poor, expensive aids that undermine home cooking at this age is bad news.

Funnily enough, the Heinz sauces seem a better bet as starter foods for young babies than many of the other jars and packets sold as full meals. They are expensive.

Milupa

Milupa produces three dried baby sauces, with added vita-mins. The three flavours are: **White, Tomato, Cheese.**

The sauces use many ingredients – 17 for cheese, 23 for white and 24 for tomato. The tomato is coloured with beet-root. By comparison, a traditional home-cooked white sauce uses butter, flour and milk.

The packs come with recipe ideas that are supposedly helpful but aren't. The one for chicken fricassee, for example, is neither labour-saving nor necessary. Before it is possible to use Milupa's White baby sauce, you must first cook the chicken, carve it, cook the mushrooms, peel the carrots, cook the carrots, boil the water for the rice, add the rice, boil the kettle, and pour the boiled water over the strained rice. After all that, you have to refill the kettle, boil the water, let it cool and mix with the gran-ules. Convenient?

Growing up with
good food

The advantages of bringing a baby on to eat the same things as the rest of the family as soon as possible are many and outweight some of the disadvantages in some foods. For a baby, this brings the sense of sharing, belonging and exploring the adult world. For parents, this means less shopping and less cooking. These are big practical pluses that compensate for any shortcomings in the diet.

In the long run, babies and children will eat what you eat and you can hardly expect a baby to happily munch away at his raw carrots while Dad is drinking a beer and eating a packet of crisps. Sue and I do not ban our children from eating fast foods. I don't like them eating foods that contain high levels of artificially induced flavours. That, to me, is the destabilising influence.

They have their own ideas. Oliver likes pasta and rice and not much else. Grace likes vegetables. Neither much likes meat, but both like sweets and chocolate, and they will talk about them at length. All you can reasonably do as a parent is to try to ensure that they experience a wide range of different foods – good as well as bad – so that they can increase their food vocabulary and, in time, make their own minds up. There is safety in variety and choice. Or at least there lies within the chance of an intelligent approach.

A balanced diet is one in which the staples – bread, pasta, rice, or potatoes – remain central and are not crowded out. Fruit and vegetables can usually hold their own, provided they do not compete directly with a bar of chocolate.

The easiest check on your diet is to monitor what goes into the shopping trolley each week. The closer it resembles a cricket match tea – sliced bread, margarine, jam, lemonade, tarts, cream cakes – the less healthy it is. On the other hand, if your trolley is full of fresh fruit, fresh vegetables and one of the four staples, the rest can probably take care of itself.

THE CASE AGAINST ADDITIVES

In 1956, after 10 years' debate over the loaf, the Minister of Agriculture, Henry Cohen, told Parliament his panel disagreed with the government's medical and scientific advisors, and with the Medical Research Council. At issue was whether bakers should bake only with the whole flour, or whether they could take out the vitamins and minerals in refining to make other products, and add supplements.

The outcome was the adulteration of the national loaf. Cohen abandoned the idea of a central standard for bread and opened the door for the additive industry. Nearly 40 years on, I believe that Mr Cohen made a serious mistake; he should have listened to his advisors.

The central issue is the impact of artificially manipulated foods in the diet. For me, issues such as sugar and salt are symptoms. The big question is whether we should allow children to be exposed to any degree to the sheer might of manipulated flavours.

If a child's first experience of strawberries is a strawberry flavour 100 times more intense; or of a potato as a millimetre-thick crisp spread with salt, vinegar and monosodium glutamate; or of muesli as maltodextrin and sugar, then that child's attitude to food is fundamentally destabilised. His or her senses have been assaulted, with the result that the more subtle flavours of nature will, unlikely, ever be appreciated.

The commercial imperative is to sell more food products. You do this by artificially increasing the levels of maximum impact – salt, sugar and other flavours. These destabilise the consumers' response which in turn destabilises the market, whicih in turn destabilises the industry, which in turn destabilises the economy. In the short term it seems like a good idea, but in the long term it is a bad idea. The health arguments are well documented. The social and political arguments have largely been ignored.

What to put
in the trolley
●●●

Which foods should you take off supermarket shelves to put into your shopping trolley? This is a fairly random list culled from different mothers of different foods they were concerned about.

✔ **BAKED BEANS** One of the great grandfathers of tinned foods and still one of the most nutritionally valuable and convenient items for the larder. Some brands lean rather heavily towards sugar, but low-sugar varieties are also marketed. **Heinz** still seems to retain its individuality among the growing competition.

✔ **BREADS** The basic white loaf has had most of the goodness taken out. Some bakers then put something back in terms of vitamins and minerals, and you get brands like **Mighty White.** At the other extreme, there is wholemeal which has everything left in it. Brown bread no longer has a classification and might be anything between those two extremes. Bread names are derived from the shape of the loaf, rather than from any other quality. Long and thin – or any other form that children can hold in their hands – invariably seems to be more successful than the traditional slice.

BREAKFAST CEREALS It is sometimes said that the only point of getting children to eat breakfast cereals is they get the milk that goes with them. While that may be true, most are so stuffed with extra vitamins, you could probably live quite a long time eating nothing else. Some cereals – ✔ **Weetabix,** ✔ **Shredded Wheat,** ✔ **Shreddies** – are conspicuously better than others. Cereal manufacturers proclaim very visibly – usually in direct proportion to the scant nutrition in the product – how much added nutrition has been put back. Ironically, healthy foods are not allowed to advertise their healthiness, because they could be perceived as medicines, while unhealthy foods can stick in one vitamin supplement and proclaim that they are the healthiest thing since sliced bread – whoops – wholemeal. ✔ **Porridge** is a better option all round, as oats are a very dynamic food. **Ready Brek** is an interesting middle-of-the-road alternative that has little sugar. ✔ **Muesli** is nutritionally sound; although, many brands – especially the so-called luxury varieties – tend to be dusted with sugar. Also, certain varieties are intended to kick-start adult systems that have grown sluggish over the years, but their levels of bran and fibre may be too high for young babies.

BEEFBURGERS The doomsday prognosis on BSE ('mad cow's disease') was so awful that all British beef-eaters should now be pushing up daisies. But the sales in the trade of mechanically recovered meat (the lowest grade of meat, which is stripped off the carcass) are buoyant, and for good reason: burgers are the cheapest form of prime protein. They have a bad press because of their fat content – not necessarily an issue for children – and often hidden sugars and other extenders. But if they persuade a child to eat a decent roll with it, then there seems little harm. Burgers are inexpensive to make at home – just mix mince with breadcrumbs (often overlooked as an inexpensive form of home nutrition), an egg and chopped onion.

BISCUITS There are three disadvantages to biscuits: sugar, hydrogenated fat, and low nutrition. That aside, they are great.

✗ CHICKEN NUGGETS AND OTHER SHAPES Deep-fried crumb products have poor credentials. They may be sources of protein, but the meat is invariably low quality. Also, the crumb-coating is often coloured, and if the nuggets have already been pre-fried, they will have taken on the fats.

CHIPS Nutritionists argue that fat chips are better for you than thin chips, because the total area exposed to the fat in frying is less and the ratio of potato is higher. Today's oven-baked chips now have surprisingly low fat content. The trick in frying is to have the fat hot enough so that it seals the potato instantly. If it is tepid, the fat just soaks into the potato. Ground-nut oil is the best value for frying at home. Much has been made of the merits of oil over dripping, but if the temperature is high enough, this probably is a side issue.

Fast food chips tend to be pre-blanched in a palm oil solution which is one of the least positive fats from a health perspective. The chips are then re-fried in the restaurant, which adds to the soak factor of fat. Often this is done with frozen or chilled chips, which lowers the temperature further and allows the chips to take a greater percentage yet of more fat.

✔ CHEDDAR Far and away the most popular cheese, and a relatively cheap source of nourishment and flavour. There is a large range of cheddars in supermarkets (in one, I counted 26), but there is little to choose between them. It is best to buy the cheapest. Vegetarian cheddars are made using non-animal rennet but tend to cost disproportionately more. Ready-grated also costs more and doesn't keep as well. Save the difference and buy a grater.

CHOCOLATE Of all the sweet things, chocolate seems to have the best credentials. Chocolate is actually bitter, but the sugar that sweetens it makes it contentious. Worldwide, baby-drink manufacturers have tried to set the limits for sugar too low to let chocolate drinks in. Although it is fattening, this is not a great issue, because most children burn up chocolate's high calorie content. Chocolate intake is also easily monitored because it is messy – unlike most other sweets – and because it is rich, which, to an extent, makes it self-regulating. The intensity of the chocolate is measured by the cocoa solids: about 20%–30% for milk chocolate and 40%–50% for plain chocolate – less harmful than the more outrageous biscuit recipes. Cocoa is also a source of vitamin B12.

✗ CRISPS Children like crisps because of their texture. They tend to prefer salt and vinegar because they appeal to two primary tastes: salt and sour. If they also have monosodium glutamate, they will appeal to what the Japanese call the fifth sense, umami. Nutritionally, crisps are worthless. Laid end to end, an average packet of crisps might stretch in a line to five feet. Both sides of that line have been deep fried, so the ratio of fat to potato is as high as it can be. Then there's the price to consider. The average packet of crisps weighs 30 grams and costs about 25p. Compare this with the equivalent weight in potatoes. The mark-up, conservatively, is about 15 times that of the raw material.

✔ **DRIED FRUITS** It is quite startling how many of the vital nutrients the body needs during pregnancy and when breast-feeding can be found in two ordinary, overlooked dried fruits. A cup of **dried apricots** could supply all the vitamin A and half the iron an adult needs. Herbalists also recommend them for detoxifying the system. The best are **Hunza,** or naturally sun-dried varieties. Be wary of some others where they may have been bleached (to preserve) with sulphur dioxide and then the colour brought back with artificial colours – which may produce an allergy if you are sensitive. Equally, they may have been lightly oiled to make them seem more attractive, but these oils can inhibit the absorption of vitamins. **Prunes,** apart from their famous role in combating constipation, have many virtues. The drying seems to concentrate their nutritional value. A cup gives a quarter of an adult's recommended daily intake of B6 and iron. They are also good sources of the trace mineral boron. This helps the absorption of calcium.

Both apricots and prunes can be eaten raw as a snack or lightly poached in a fruit salad.

FAST FOODS Fish and chips are a solid, reliable form of fast-food, provided the oil they are fried in is hot. Also, the coating should not be – as is so beloved of department store cooking – a yellow overcoat of additives. Chips should be thick cut. The equation of fish and potatoes equals fat is not too one-sided. Pizza houses can probably claim to offer the healthiest fast-food, because of the amount of bread dough in a pizza. But children may dislike the acidity in many of the toppings. The problem with hamburgers is that where they began life as perfectly acceptable ratios of bread to meat with some greenery in the relish, the sugar levels have been raised to exceptional levels in the buns. Chips, generally, are so thin that – like crisps – they have high fat content. Generally, people are aware of the dangers of eating too much fried food, which may be why Kentucky Fried Chicken changed its name to KFC.

FROZEN FOODS Some foods freeze really well. Peas are probably a better buy in their frozen state than when they are fresh or tinned, and they a dependable stand-by. If it is frozen, white fish is often a more useful buy. It will have been frozen at sea, retaining much of its nutrients. It is best cooked straight from frozen without thawing. Bread keeps well in the freezer, and a couple of spare French loaves or the part-baked and frozen rolls are useful. Sweetcorn is probably better in tins, and the best carrots are fresh. Freeze-dried herbs are not a patch on fresh. Meat freezes well enough, but the time taken to defrost it makes it a bit of a performance. It is better to make up sauces – mince into bolognese, for example, – before freezing.

ICE-CREAM Because it so cold, the quantity of sugar in ice-cream is easily overlooked. The same applies to ice-lollies. There are two generations, both of which have their draw-backs: one is cream and eggs; the other is not cream and eggs but has a lot of substitutes. Also, you've got to be careful where you buy your ice-cream. Health checks on ice-cream vans have consistently found poor hygiene.

JAMS There is little point in checking the ingredients for extra sugar on cans of baked beans if you smear jam on your child's toast each morning. Jam is, after all, 50% sugar. There have been great leaps forwards in jam-making in the past few years; although the sugar levels in some are so low that they cannot be called jam. As a result they are given peculiar names, such as 'Very Very Strawberry'. Sadly, most of our bread is so dull that it needs jam (and butter). The smart move is to seek out better, more interesting breads, such as a good French loaf.

✗ MARGARINE OR BUTTER? It does not follow that children will want either margarine or butter on their bread, and if you get them into the habit of eating interesting breads, they might make the leap away from fats more easily than you. The margarine economy is a false one – most of the saving goes towards buying the water that bulks it up. The health arguments against butter are looking increasingly dubious, and the process of hydrogenating the liquid fats so that they are hard makes the unsaturated fats saturated. I wouldn't give my child margarine or similar spreads.

✔ PASTA The great stand-by, and almost universally popular. The quicker-cook spaghettis are just thinner, so they aren't really any cheaper. The only saving made is in the time it takes to prepare them. Alphabet shapes are popular with older children. Cans are marginally quicker and more convenient, but they are more expensive. The sauces tend to be bland and high in sugar.

✔ PIZZA Enjoys the reputation of being the healthiest of the fast foods because of the high ratio of bread to topping. Originally, they were the off-bits of dough rolled out by the baker's wife. The more pungent toppings on many pizzas – anchovies, olives, even tomatoes – may not appeal to younger children; nor will the heat of the melted mozzarella. Check the ingredients of the toppings on packet versions. Home-made pizzas using French bread, ketchup and cheddar baked in the oven for a few minutes are inexpensive.

✔ RICE Children often like rice as a main dish as well as in rice pudding. Invariably, the bigger the packet of rice you buy, the cheaper the cost per serving. The lowest prices can be found at Indian and Chinese supermarkets. Fragrant Thai rice is one of the best main-line rices available. By comparison, American Long Grain. Easy Cook and In The Bag tend to lose some of the nutrients in processing. Pudding rices tend to be shorter, flatter and more bland, but they are good bases to introduce seasonings, such as vanilla. Ground rice is similar to rice flour.

SAUSAGES Very good finger-food, and children who dislike other meats usually eat sausages. The basic cheap sausages may have only 65% meat, which can include fat and skin. The smoother and pinker versions tend to be heavily processed, while the new generation of more expensive, traditional sausages have texture and a higher proportion (up to 85%) of quality meat.

SOUPS So many people have taught themselves to be good cooks by starting with soups that it is perhaps unwise to recommend short-cuts. It is cheaper and more convenient to cook soups at home, provided you are organised and have the time and confidence. Canned soups tend to be expensive and erratic with a few notable exceptions. Tetrapaks of baby soups from **Boots** are very expensive – about the same as a pint of beer. The tomato version is so unappealing that, if you taste it, you will be encouraged to start making your own.

More interesting are the new generation of fresh soups started by the **Covent Garden Soup** company and brilliantly imitated by own labels, such as **Tesco**. Dried soups are for mountaineers and campers only.

SPREADS If children are eating bread, does it matter what goes on top of it? In many cases, the alternative spreads are often more worthwhile than straight jam. The new generation of chocolate spreads are inviting to children. **Sainsbury** does a good one. Savoury spreads such as **Marmite** seem to be an acquired taste. The best peanut butters are the intense **Schmuckers** and the looser, more peanut-textured **Skippy**. As for honey, it is reliably sweet – the best should say on the label what kind of flowers the bees pollinated; the rest are just homogenised mixes. Considering the wide use of pesticides, it might be best to buy honey from areas without intensive agriculture. The only difference between clear and set varieties is temperature. Then there are treacle and golden syrup, which are very sweet.

✗ SWEETS Inevitable sooner or later. Most of the cases of allergic reaction are related to the colourants, especially the tartrazines, in the reds and the yellows. Some sweets have gone to the lengths of including vitamin supplements. The levels of sugar and other additives are difficult to judge, especially when sold loose. Most are neat doses of sugar and glucose syrup. **Tesco** and **Sainsbury** have moved sweets away from check-out areas so that children are not tempted to pick 'n' mix on every shopping trip. Other shops should follow their move.

✔ TINNED FISH For the most part, tinned fish is not as good as fresh fish. But oily fish, such as sardines, are more widely available in tinned form. Also, they are cheaper – pilchards are one of the cheapest foods in supermarkets – and good sources of omega three, which nutritionists are increasingly keen on. Sardines and mackerel are prime sources. Tinned tuna is the one exception, as its omega three oils seem to be destroyed in the processing. The smoked versions have concentrated omega three levels and are even better, but they shouldn't be fed to young children, as they don't respond well to smoked flavours. Sometimes, though, they like the milder cures of kippers.

✔ YOGHURTS AND FROMAGE FRAIS The price tends to go up according to how much fat is in them, and multi-packs are prone to erratic pricing policies, which are not always the bargain they seem. Few of the small pots can actually claim the health benefits traditionally associated with yoghurts. These are usually marked BA, denoting bifidus acidophilus (live cultures). But usually these are too sour to appeal to children. The cultures are different for yoghurts and fromage frais, but these have low fat or have no fat milk with flavours. Yoghurts, it is argued, are more easily digested than milk, because their curds stay in the stomach longer. Both yoghurts and fromage frais are prime sources of calcium – yoghurts having more because the whey is separated. Yoghurts are long on vitamin D; fromage frais on vitamins A and B12. Yoghurts with fruit purée, rather than just flavourings, are probably more nutritious, but they have more sugar. Also, they tend to be smaller. Possibly the best thing about them is that they are a more acceptable alternative to the more gunky, fat-laden whips and creams.

Be on the
safe side

● ●

Probably standards of hygiene were much worse 30 years ago, but the risks were localised. Now that companies expect to sell their products to all 60 million of us, and probably further afield as well, the dangers are multiplied. Even if foods are safer, statistically the dangers are greater. When you are pregnant or have young children in the house there are some dangers which are greater than normal. The main areas to be careful about are:

THE FRIDGE Raw meat should be kept on the bottom shelf so it does not drip on to other foods. The fridge should be cold enough. Unlike cooking, fridges cannot make foods safe, only keep them safe. Ready meals, ready made salads and cooked meats should be put in the fridge as quickly as possible. If they sit around in a warm office all afternoon, or the back of a car, bacteria can start to develop. Most kitchen designs have fridges that are too small for safe modern shopping; and in many cases the fridges are not cold enough. In some countries manufacturers have to put thermometers in the fridge by law.

FOOD POISONING Although the new hygiene laws are much tougher than before, it is probably also true that we have less resistance to food poisoning because so much of what we eat is sanitised. The high risk foods are often those found in sandwich bars – for example, mayonnaise fillings, cooked cold meats and salads kept above chill temperatures. Cold foods are more dangerous than hot ones. This is especially relevant if you are pregnant – see salmonella and listeria, below.

WORK SURFACES In all probability our bodies get used to the kind of bacteria that live in kitchens. Work surfaces nevertheless are a potential danger.

❖ Be wary of using the same chopping board for raw meat as for vegetables, or using the same knife without washing it in-between.

❖ Allowing cats or dogs to live in the kitchen.

❖ Letting foods, especially meat dishes, sit around at room temperature so that bacteria grows.

SALMONELLA Salmonella affects everyone. It is one of the commonest forms of food poisoning and is particularly unpleasant, causing sickness and diarrhoea. Mothers are warned to be watchful from the start of pregnancy.

❖ **Eggs** are the biggest concern. Government medical advice is strict – pregnant women and young children should only eat eggs cooked so that the white and yolk are solid. This includes recipes in which the egg may be only partly cooked, say in sauces, or not cooked at all, as in homemade mayonnaise. It is possible to buy pasteurised powdered eggs and cartons of pasteurised yolks but they are not widely stocked and recipes are in short supply. Shop-bought mayonnaises are made with pasteurised eggs and are perfectly safe.

❖ **Chicken and other raw meat** can contain food poisoning bacteria which are normally killed in the cooking. Chicken especially should be cooked through so there are no pink bits by the bone. The best test is to slip a knife or fork into the thigh bone of a roasting chicken. If the juices run clear then it is cooked but, if there is any sign of pinkness, put it back in the oven. It is also risky for you to handle raw meat. Wash your hands carefully and also wash the chopping board you are working on before moving on to any other foods or jobs.

LISTERIA Listeria is perhaps the most frightening of all food-related diseases if you are pregnant, although the figures have started to fall away since the dangers have been recognised. In extreme cases, listeria can kill. It affects pregnant women and may be associated with any number of miscarriages. But it is a secretive disease and the incubation period of six weeks often makes tracking down the cause difficult. It also affects those with low immune systems – like babies. The rest of us

TOXOPLASMOSIS

Toxoplasmosis can affect babies. It is caught from eating raw or undercooked meat, unpasteurised milk, or from contact with cat's faeces. There are some simple rules that cut out most of the risks. Keep work surfaces clean, especially after handling raw meat, always cook meat thoroughly and wash fruit and vegetables. If you have cats, wear rubber gloves when cleaning the litter tray, and also wear gloves when gardening.

can carry on gaily without worrying – which is why it has taken so long to recognize the dangers since it was first identified in 1925. Official figures suggest it only affects 1 in 30,000; but that is a percentage of all the population, not only those who are pregnant. Some foods are known to harbour higher levels of bacteria:

❖ **Ripened soft and blue cheeses** – notably Camembert and Brie – have high levels of bacteria. Hard cheeses like Cheddar are quite safe, while unpasteurised cheeses are often wrongly linked to listeria. The other bacteria in unpasteurised cheese probably restrict the listeria. If listeria is in a cheese, it will probably be near or in the skin so, if in doubt, cut this part away.

❖ **Pâté** is an ideal breeding ground for listeria and should be avoided – although tinned pâtés will be fine. The danger is more in how they are stored. Tins are safe; other packaging is not.

❖ **Cook-chill meals** and any other foods that are kept at ambient temperatures can be a risk. It is the way food is kept rather than what it is that matters. If food is ready to eat – so that you wouldn't wash it – and has been kept in a well-lit display cabinet, then there may be a risk even if the cabinet was refrigerated. Foods kept at the wrong temperature are just as dangerous as high-bacteria foods – for example, one of the worst cases of listeria on record concerned coleslaw. Shop refrigerators and display cabinets should have a thermometer on them and it is worth checking that the shelves are being kept cool enough if you use one shop regularly. The shop should be happy to instal thermometers if it doesn't have them already. If it doesn't, it could be liable and be closed down.

You only have to
look at the label

The laws on labelling are about to change. Until now manufacturers have only had to give details of energy, protein, carbohydrate and fat on given foods. Nothing else has to be put on the label, unless the company makes a health claim which they have to justify.

From now on, if a company says a product is low in salt then the label has to show the amount of salt; or if they say that it is high in vitamin A then the label has to show the quantity. In many cases these claims do not bear much examination and have often been made even when, say, salt levels or vitamin levels are not conspicuously different.

As of October 1995 any foods making any claims at all will have to give details of all the relevant levels of sugar, salt, saturates and fibre.

In the case of sugars the total will be rounded up to include the natural sugars as well as any added sugars to make comparisons easier. The irony is that these claims cannot be made about many ordinary foods that are known to be beneficial – like oats or apples – because nothing is added to them.

What the *names mean*

ADDITIVES are banned in baby foods. But some E numbers can still be found – for example, E300 is vitamin C.

ARTIFICIAL SWEETENERS are not allowed by law in baby foods. Low-calorie and diet drinks are also outlawed.

BRAN is too bulky for babies to cope with, and this can stop the absorption of vitamins in the food. High-level bran foods are not usually recommended for children under five.

CASEINATE is spray dried milk protein used to thicken and add bulk to foods. Its major benefit is it offers some texture but, otherwise, there is no real reason to use it.

CALCIUM CARBONATE is mineral salt used to preserve the colour of foods and neutralise the acidity. It is probably unnecessary.

CHLAMYDIOSIS is a rare disease caught from sheep in labour or new-born lambs and can cause miscarriages. Sheep can also carry listeria.

CITRIC ACID is used to stop foods going off. It is cheap but vacuum packing food with nitrogen is a better alternative.

COLIC is not thought to be related to diet.

DEMINERALISED WHEY is a by-product of cheese-making, used to add bulk and texture.

FLAVOUR is a term frequently used on food packaging. A label that declares the product has orange flavour need not explain by law that it contains no orange at all. Drinks and foods that contain orange will be called Orange Flavoured.

GOAT'S MILK products for babies have been banned in the UK since 1993. Cases have been recorded of babies suffering from anaemia when they have been fed solely on goat's milk, which has little folic acid.

HYDROGENATED VEGETABLE FAT increases the calories in food and stabilises the other ingredients. Hydrogenation changes the fluid fats to hard fats. The disadvantage is it also changes the unsaturated fats to saturated fats and creates what are fashionably called trans-fatty acids. It is used because it is a cheap source of energy and a preservative. Critics argue that vacuum packing or flushing the sachet to remove the oxygen is a better means of keeping the food safe.

LECITHIN is extracted from egg yolks and used as an emulsifier to mix fat and water. Usually its presence is a sign that the other ingredients may not be particularly good quality and invariably suggests there are hidden fats.

MALTODEXTRIN is a name given to any of a range of complex carbohydrates that have been partially broken down so that babies can digest them more easily. They break up further in the body and provide sugars for energy. They are used in some foods to give a smooth, creamy texture, with the starch turning to sugar in the mouth. However, it has been suggested that, over a period, they may encourage tooth decay. The body absorbs maltodextrins more slowly than other sugars, which allows them to deliver an optimum level of nutrients. This has led to their increased use in sports drinks. They are also used by hospitals for treating patients with, for example, severe burns. They are a 'safe' food in the sense that they pass all the worldwide restrictions on what can and cannot be fed to babies. (But see page 12.)

MICROWAVES cook unevenly. Hot spots can scald a baby's mouth. If you have to use a microwave for making up baby foods, ensure the food is well mixed and left to cool for some time.

MINERAL WATERS: A baby's system cannot tolerate bottled waters, which contain high levels of minerals and salts. A number of companies have got round this legislation by selling flavoured, de-mineralised waters. They are expensive but convenient drinks.

MORNING SICKNESS: One remedy is to eat a dry biscuit or to have a small drink before getting up. Fizzy waters and fizzy drinks can help. Avoid heavy meals and greasy foods.

NUTS are usually best not given to children until they are five, because of the risk of choking. If you are using peanut butters, choose a smooth variety.

SALT: Avoid. Babies' kidneys cannot tolerate high levels of salt, which can build up in the blood. The maximum amount of salt allowed in commercial weaning foods is 200mg for every 100g of ready-to-eat baby food, 300mg for every 100g of rusk, and 100mg for every 100g of ready-to-eat cereal. Many ordinary foods naturally contain fractional levels of salt. These will not harm a baby, but some foods – such as hard cheese, which use salts as preservatives – should not be given to babies until they are at least six months old.

SHEEP'S MILK is not recommended for babies less than 12 months old, and often as old as 18 months.

SKIMMED MILK POWDER is a cheap form of energy and protein found in most infant breakfast cereals, which makes the mix go creamy. But, as the milk itself is not used in baby foods because of the imbalance of proteins and vitamins, these have to be added in other forms. Some have suggested a link to the rise in allergies in young babies with the increased use of skimmed milk powders. But the strongest argument against it is simply that it is a cheap bulk ingredient of questionable value.

SWEETS: The manufacturers themselves admit that children under two should not eat sweets. Apart from anything else, small teeth are tricky to clean. Then there is the contentious issue of whether to expose young children to the full power of artificial flavours.

UNPASTEURISED MILK is sometimes called 'green milk'. This should not be given to babies, because of the risk of infection.

WATER SOFTENERS: Avoid. Water softeners often use sodium chloride or salt to soften hard water.

The baby food
who's who

The baby food market is dominated by a small number of companies, most of whom believe that they need a pan-European market to survive.

Outsiders who have tried to break in have come up against unusual odds. They have no access to the network of midwives and health visitors who are one of the main communicators of information on baby food. Research has shown that the majority of new mothers listen most to their mother. If mum bought Cow and Gate, then daughter follows. Parts of the industry are holding their breath as the first generation of Milupa mothers – first introduced in the 70's – start to proffer advice to their pregnant daughters. Milupa is hoping this will start a major swing to its dry goods.

Baby food companies are also different from other food companies. They have become defensive and innured by years of potential legislation. They are hidebound by strict moralistic attitudes that have neutered them. They may declare that they have the so-and-so Mother and Baby Nutritional Advice Centre based on 60 years of practical experience, but those diligent mums who bother to write off to those so-called august centres receive mostly nothing better than a glossy pamphlet prepared by a PR agency.

Mothers spend nearly £300 million on baby foods each year. But as the birth rate has been falling, manufacturers have been trying to expand a static market. As the market analysts, Euromonitor, puts it: [these companies] are introducing a variety of products for older babies to [keep] consumers in the baby food market for longer.

Baby Organix

was started in 1992 by Jane Dick and Lizzie Van with the logo 'Pure Foods, Healthy Babies, A Safer World.' "We were appalled to find that British baby food was dominated by bland, poor quality imaginatively described junk food for babies." Neither have children. Jane has a background in the chemical industry and Lizzie had worked in the food industry. They committed the company to sourcing organic foods – 95% of all the ingredients meet Soil Association standards – and avoiding extenders and additives especially hydrogenated vegetable fats, maltodextrin, sucrose, dextrose and skimmed milk powders. They went for challenging recipes combining interesting flavours. Their products are now stocked in most supermarkets. The range starts at 4 months, with the more cereal-based foods for the slightly older. The cereals can also be bought mail order in boxes of six: free phone 0800 393511 for details. Postage £1 on orders under £25. Mixed cases available.

Farley's

was owned by Glaxo until 1986 when it was bought by Boots and has been sold to Heinz in 1994. It has had a troubled decade with some spectacular advertising goofs – notably the survey that suggested that breastfeeding stopped women resuming their sex lives ("breasts are more than just feeding machines"). It is alleged that at different times it has also given donations of money and gifts to doctors and hospitals. Contentiously, in a UK campaign it asked breastfeeding mothers to compare the formulas against their own milk. It was acquired by Heinz, principally, it is thought, because Heinz also owns a bottle company (Camera). The first indications are that Heinz is sorting Farley's out. In the autumn of 1994 the sugar-laden Bed Timers range was withdrawn following pressure because of the high sugar content.

Heinz

was started by Henry J in Sharpsburg, Pennsylvania in the 1860s. Henry was a tough campaigner against adulterated foods and sold his range in clear glass jars so people could see what they were getting. The baby range was launched in the UK in the 1930s. They began with just 14 varieties – included strained beets and the range has now been extended to over

100. In 1993 more than one third of all the recipes were modified and changed. Heinz now controls 60 per cent of all wet baby meals. Pure baby juices and sauces were introduced in 1994.

Milupa

is based in Friedrichsdorf near Frankfurt, Germany. Originally a bakery, it began to granulate its products and swiftly moved to adding milk and fruit for baby foods. It opened in the UK in 1973 and at the same time the parent company became part of a conglomerate specialising in technology and pharmaceuticals, Altana, based in Bad Homburg. Milupa has factories in Germany, France, Spain and Portugal. There is no UK production. It is the market leader in dry cereals, formula milks and herbal drinks. It is also prominent in pharmacies. It sells nearly 50 different products mostly targeted in the 3 months to 8 months range. Its main concerns recently have been about sugar. Marketing campaigns are often based around free sampling. On ethical issues it purports to support breastfeeding, although it produces infant formula. It says it only sells to countries where the World Health Organisation guidelines on baby care products are adhered to; however, formula campaigners cite numerous examples, which may have some truth, of the company advertising, giving free samples and selling foods and drinks to mothers of young babies.

Cow & Gate/Nutricia

is part of the Dutch company NV Veneridge Bedrijven Nutricia, the second largest baby milk manufacturer in Europe and the leading manufacturer of baby foods in the UK. **Olvarit** is the other big brand name. It covers all areas of the market except rusks. It is proficient in selling direct with money-off coupons, samplings and offers. Formula campaigners cite instances of poor labelling, direct marketing at mothers, free samples and non-factual promotion to health workers.

Boots

is the only major chemist to have developed its own label for baby foods. It began on the 1970s. It is claimed that the **First Harvest** range uses traditional farming methods with companion planting and crop rotation and that livestock is humanely reared. The organic range, **Mother's Recipes** is certified by the Soil Association. While other drinks manufacturers have moved to change the labelling to avoid the confusion of lumping hidden sugars under the labelling carbohydrates, Boots own-label drinks have been the last not to declare the sugar content.

Robinson's

brand name goes back to 1823 when Mathais Robinson began producing patent barley as a powder for kidney complaints and patent groats as an early infant food. In 1863 the company was taken over by Keen and Son, the first manufacturer of mustard in London, and in turn were taken over by Colman's of Norwich, on the strength of the mustard and spice business. The first baby drinks were introduced in 1971 – strawberry, raspberry, rosehip, orange and blackcurrant flavours. Pure baby fruit juices came in 1982. The tetra pack carton came in 1986.

Safeway

was the first UK retailer to develop its own-label baby food. The group has been put together as a mish mash of smaller high street retailers but increasingly aspires to the kind of fresh food, large store of Sainsbury's and Tesco. The range is sensibly safe and follows the big retailers' creed of attracting mothers in by cutting the price of nappies.

Sainsbury's

after many years of avoiding the issue, went into baby foods in the autumn of 1994 with a full range. It has a reputation for high class, own-label products. The packaging is brilliant but the thinking behind the range is old-fashioned with a worrying dependence on maltodextrin in its dried foods. Better to buy the fresh food in the first aisle.

WYETH and SMA Nutrition

The original Wyeth company was a pharmacy in Philadelphia that produced sweet elixirs. But it was among the first to patent potions for prescription and not make them to order. It developed the first pressed tablets. On the back of these products it has become a world leader in medical research and commerce (at one point dominating 60% of the world penicillin market), – still being a major force in oral contraceptives, and having developed freeze-dried smallpox vaccine. The infant milks are sold against the medicinal backdrop, not so much as foods, but as medicines. SMA stands for Scientific Milk Adaptation, developed originally in 1915 when the butterfat was replaced with other fats closer to those in breast milk. The company was taken over by Wyeth in 1937 but it was not until as recently as 1962 that Wyeth developed the system of using electrodialysis to demineranise whey from cow's milk. It is the second largest infant formula producer in the world and has been highly criticised and boycotted for selling formulas with English labelling to non-English speaking countries, and using aggressive advertising in the third world which would not be allowed in the UK. Examples of this are a picture of a young girl chess player taking on a teenager under the caption: 'Some minds are fed earlier than most.', or an advertisement in an Asian edition of a medical magazine 'For the World Infants only the best is good enough." The last example was as recent as 1993.

Index *Suppliers*

Index *General*

Tell us what you think

Being a parent is a full-time occupation. But if you can find the time to share the experiences you have had feeding your children, the advice could be invaluable to new mothers. The foods available are always changing, and so are circumstances. And maybe there are some problems that have come up that this small book has not dealt with. Let me know and we will try and revise the book so that other mothers can benefit from your hard-earned knowledge and thus benefit their children. Please write to:

Drew Smith
^c/o Department BD,
HarperCollins*Publishers*,
77–85 Fulham Palace Road,
Hammersmith,
London W6 8JB.

ALSO BY DREW SMITH

This book should be available from booksellers, but in case of difficulty please write to: HarperCollins Mail Order, Dept 2, Westerhill Road, Glasgow G64 2QT, or telephone 0141 772 2281.